General Chemistry: Nassau Community College

CHE 107 Lab Manual

3rd Edition

Douglas S. Cody I Edward R. Shenal
Editors

CENGAGE
Learning™

Australia • Brazil • Japan • Korea • Mexico • Singapore • Spain • United Kingdom • United States

CENGAGE
Learning™

General Chemistry: Nassau Community College
CHE 107 Lab Manual
3rd Edition

Douglas S. Cody | Edward R. Shenal
Editors

Executive Editors:
 Michele Baird

 Maureen Staudt

 Michael Stranz

Project Development Manager:
 Linda deStefano

Senior Marketing Coordinators:
 Sara Mercurio

 Lindsay Shapiro

Production/Manufacturing Manager:
 Donna M. Brown

PreMedia Services Supervisor:
 Rebecca A. Walker

Rights & Permissions Specialist:
 Kalina Hintz

Cover Image:
 Getty Images*

* Unless otherwise noted, all cover images used by Custom Solutions, a part of Cengage Learning, have been supplied courtesy of Getty Images with the exception of the Earthview cover image, which has been supplied by the National Aeronautics and Space Administration (NASA).

© 2003 Cengage Learning

ALL RIGHTS RESERVED. No part of this work covered by the copyright herein may be reproduced, transmitted, stored or used in any form or by any means graphic, electronic, or mechanical, including but not limited to photocopying, recording, scanning, digitizing, taping, Web distribution, information networks, or information storage and retrieval systems, except as permitted under Section 107 or 108 of the 1976 United States Copyright Act, without the prior written permission of the publisher.

For product information and technology assistance, contact us at
Cengage Learning Customer & Sales Support, 1-800-354-9706

For permission to use material from this text or product,
submit all requests online at **cengage.com/permissions**
Further permissions questions can be emailed to
permissionrequest@cengage.com

ISBN-13: 978-0-7593-2615-6

ISBN-10: 0-7593-2615-0

Cengage Learning
5191 Natorp Boulevard
Mason, Ohio 45040
USA

Cengage Learning is a leading provider of customized learning solutions with office locations around the globe, including Singapore, the United Kingdom, Australia, Mexico, Brazil, and Japan. Locate your local office at:
international.cengage.com/region

Cengage Learning products are represented in Canada by Nelson Education, Ltd.

For your lifelong learning solutions, visit **custom.cengage.com**

Visit our corporate website at **cengage.com**

Printed in the United States of America

Custom Contents

LABORATORY EQUIPMENT

MASS MEASUREMENT EQUIPMENT

Balances are used for measuring mass (Figures LE.1 through LE.4 show the types of balances you most likely will use.) We can classify all types of balances as either digital or nondigital. Digital balances vary widely in the degree of accuracy of the mass measurements they provide; however, because of the similarity of their operation, we will classify all digital balances together here to distinguish them from the nondigital types. Digital balances are generally top loading, and those that are accurate to the nearest 0.0001 g (0.1 mg) are suitable for analytical work.

There are several types of nondigital balances you might encounter: the top loader, the triple-beam balance, and the analytical balance. You will use balances throughout your laboratory work. Experiment 1 will introduce you to the balances your instructor has chosen for your laboratory program.

There is a significant distinction between mass and weight, but in this lab manual we will use the verb *weigh* to refer to the act of determining mass. You should refer to your text if you are not familiar with the distinction between mass and weight.

Weighing by Difference. The mass measurement of most chemicals is done using a process known as *weighing by difference.* In this technique, an empty vessel is weighed, filled with the substance in question, and then reweighed. The mass of the empty vessel is called the *tare.* The difference in the two readings represents the mass of the substance. For example, the mass of a sample of sodium chloride might be determined by weighing an empty beaker, adding some sodium chloride to the beaker, and reweighing the beaker plus sodium chloride. Thus, if an empty beaker has a mass (tare) of 30.4 g, and the beaker plus some sodium chloride has a mass of 32.7 g, the mass of the sodium chloride must be:

$$32.7 \text{ g} - 30.4 \text{ g} = 2.3 \text{ g}$$

The reliable operation of a laboratory balance requires that it be kept clean, therefore, *you should never weigh a substance directly on the balance pan.* If you spill a substance on the balance during weighing, clean it up immediately.

Zero Adjustment. All balances have a weighing pan on which you place the object to be weighed. Every balance also has some type of *zero adjustment.* This adjustment enables you to set the balance at zero, that is, to zero the balance when the weighing pan is empty. In the descriptions of the balances that follow, we usually will describe the operation of the zero adjustment last, after explaining how to read the balance.

The Digital Balance

The digital balance (Fig. LE.1) is the easiest balance to use. Simply turn the balance on and press the "zero" bar. This bar is the zero adjustment, and pressing it will set the digital readout to zero. Next, place the object to be weighed on the weighing pan, and read the digital readout. This reading represents the mass of the object. You may observe that the last digit on the readout fluctuates over time. That fluctuation represents the uncertainty in the measurement at that digit. When taking a reading, select the value that represents the middle of the observed range of values. Experiment 1 will draw your attention to uncertainty in measurements of all kinds.

Many digital balances have a *tare function* that automatically takes into account the tare of the beaker or flask being used. If a weighing is to be made by difference, press the tare bar after placing the empty vessel on the weighing pan. This will reset the digital readout to zero. Now if a substance is added to the vessel, the digital reading will be the actual mass of the substance in the vessel.

The Nondigital Top Loader

The nondigital top loader operates in essentially the same fashion as the digital balance, except that a scale must be read and interpreted. Figure LE.2 shows a typical top-loading balance capable of measuring mass to the nearest 0.01 g. The pointer on the right side of the scale shows the mass to be read. In the example shown, the mass is somewhere between 49.3 g and 49.4 g. By estimating the last significant digit, the mass can be read as 49.34 g. Depending upon your own estimate, you might perceive this reading to be closer to either 49.33 g or 49.35 g.

The zero adjustment on the model in Figure LE.2 is near the bottom of the face of the balance, as shown. To zero the balance, turn the knob clockwise or counterclockwise (with the weighing pan empty) until the pointer reads exactly zero.

FIGURE LE.1
Digital balance. The scale reads 146.38 g.

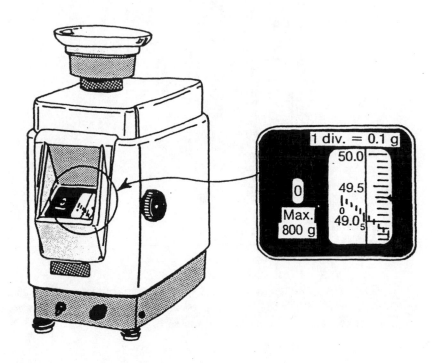

FIGURE LE.2
Top-loading balance. The scale reads 49.34 g.

The Triple-beam Balance

Triple-beam balances vary in the degree of accuracy to which they are capable of making mass measurements. The platform balance shown in Figure LE.3 is typical of such balances. These balances are operated similarly to those used for weighing patients in a doctor's office. After the balance has been zeroed, the object to be weighed is placed on the weighing pan. The movable weights on the three bars are added or subtracted (moved right or left) until the pointer at the right-hand end of the bars points to the zero point on the vertical scale to the right of the balance. In actual practice, the pointer is allowed to oscillate up and down until its swing above the zero point is equal to its swing below the zero point. The balance shown in Figure LE.3 reads 312.0 g.

FIGURE LE.3
Triple-beam balance. The scale reads 312.0 g.

3

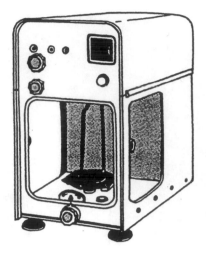

FIGURE LE.4
Analytical balance.

The zero adjustment on the triple-beam balance consists of an adjustable nut on a screw. With the weighing pan empty, the nut is screwed clockwise or counterclockwise until the balance reads zero.

The Nondigital Analytical Balance

The analytical balance (Fig. LE.4) is a very delicate instrument that must be treated with considerable care. Because of the sensitivity of the analytical balance, weighings are carried out in a closed chamber that is free from drafts. The actual directions for using a nondigital analytical balance are sufficiently detailed that we will leave it to your instructor to describe the operation of this type of analytical balance if you will be using one in your laboratory work.

VOLUME MEASUREMENT EQUIPMENT

A variety of equipment is available for the measurement of volume. The experiments described in this laboratory manual include the use of the graduated cylinder, the volumetric flask, and the buret. You may also encounter the pipet in your future laboratory work.

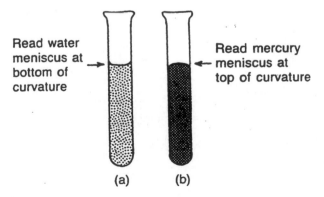

Read water meniscus at bottom of curvature

Read mercury meniscus at top of curvature

(a)   (b)

FIGURE LE.5
Meniscus. (a) Water meniscus. (b) Mercury meniscus.

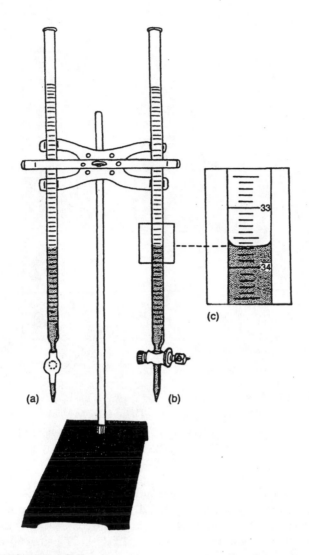

FIGURE LE.7
*Buret. (a) Mohr type buret. (b) Typical buret with stopcock. (c) The meniscus
shown reads 33.67 mL.*

with one of two types of stopcock or valve. A Mohr type of buret uses a valve
constructed of a piece of rubber tubing with a glass bead inside. This simple
valve connects the bottom of the buret to the glass drip tip through which the
solution is dispensed (Fig. LE.7a). The glass bead must fit snugly inside the
rubber tubing to prevent leaking. To dispense solution from the buret, pinch or
squeeze the rubber tubing to pull it away from the glass bead, allowing the
solution to flow. As soon as you release the tubing, the pressure of the rubber
tubing around the bead stops the flow of the solution. A more expensive type of
buret is constructed with a valve known as a stopcock that can be turned like a
faucet to control the flow of solution (Fig. LE.7b).

Figure LE.7c shows where to read a buret. As with the graduated cylinder,
it is important to have your eye at the same level as the meniscus to avoid reading errors. Notice that the numbers are largest at the bottom of the buret.
Always estimate the most accurate decimal place the buret is capable of
providing. Burets are generally calibrated in milliliters. The meniscus shown in
Figure LE.7c would be read as 33.67 mL.

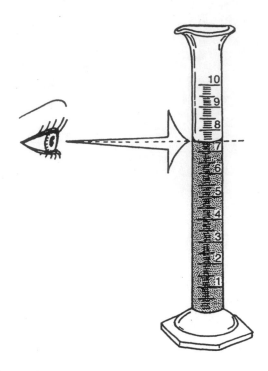

FIGURE LE.6
Reading a graduated cylinder. To obtain the correct reading, your eye must be level with the meniscus. The meniscus shown reads 7.5 mL.

To obtain a volume reading from any of these pieces of equipment, you must identify and correctly read a curved surface known as the *meniscus*, which is illustrated in Figure LE.5. The meniscus of water, and of solutions made with water, is concave downward (Fig. LE.5a). When reading a water meniscus, take the reading at the very bottom of the meniscus. To use certain pieces of laboratory equipment, you must be able to read a mercury meniscus, which is convex (Fig. LE.5b). When reading a mercury meniscus, take the reading at the very top.

The Graduated Cylinder
Graduated cylinders are available in a wide range of sizes. To read the volume in a graduated cylinder, your eye must be directly across from the meniscus. If you look down from above or up from below, a phenomenon known as *parallax* will cause false readings of the meniscus. In addition, always read the scale on a graduated cylinder to the maximum degree possible. This will involve an estimate of the last digit. For example, the meniscus shown in Figure LE.6 would be read as 7.5 mL. You will use the graduated cylinder frequently in your experimental work. This piece of equipment is introduced to you in Experiment 1.

The Buret
A buret is a cylindrical graduated tube used for dispensing solutions and measuring the volume of solution dispensed (Fig. LE.7). Burets are most often used in a technique known as *titration*, in which the volumes of reacting solutions are measured.

All burets are equipped with either a stopcock or valve that permits the controlled flow of solution out of the buret. You are likely to encounter burets

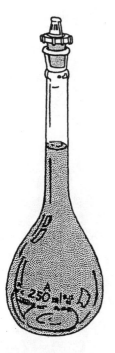

FIGURE LE.8
Volumetric flask.

The volume dispensed by a buret is determined by the difference in the readings obtained before and after the solution is dispensed. It is not necessary to fill a buret exactly to the zero graduation. Instead, the liquid level may be brought anywhere near the top of the graduated scale, and the reading recorded. A quantity of solution is then dispensed, and the graduated scale is read a second time. The volume of solution dispensed is the difference between the two readings.

To prepare a buret for use, it may be necessary first to rinse the buret with small portions of the solution about to be dispensed before filling the buret. This is especially true if the buret has just been cleaned and is wet. To rinse the buret, pour about 5 mL of the solution into the buret. Tip the buret into an almost horizontal position, and allow the solution to wet the sides of the buret completely by rotating the buret in your hands. Finally, turn the buret upright again, and drain the solution through the drip tip to complete the rinsing. Repeat this procedure a second time, and then fill the buret near to the top of its graduated section. As mentioned, it is not necessary to fill the buret to the zero mark. The use of the buret is applied in Experiments 16 and 17.

The Volumetric Flask

Volumetric flasks are pear-shaped flasks used for preparing solutions whose concentrations are accurately known (Fig. LE.8). These pieces of glassware come in a wide variety of sizes, ranging from one milliliter up to several liters. Every volumetric flask is calibrated individually with a line on its neck. When the liquid level inside the flask is filled so that the meniscus sits on the calibration line, the volume of the contents is equal to the stated volume of the flask. It is possible to prepare solutions whose concentrations are accurately known by carefully weighing a sample of solute into a volumetric flask and then diluting to the calibration line. The use of the volumetric flask is applied in Experiment 16.

DISTILLED WATER AND WASH BOTTLES

Your various laboratory investigations will require the use of water for a variety of purposes. For some of these, the water will not be one of the chemicals whose properties you are investigating, nor will it be mixed with those chemicals as a solvent. For example, several of the experiments described in this manual call for the use of a hot water bath. A test tube or flask containing the substances under investigation will be set into the water bath, but the substances themselves will not come into contact with the water. In this case, ordinary tap water should be used.

Most often when you are asked to use water, the water either will be one of the substances being studied, or it will be mixed with the substances under investigation. Since ordinary tap water contains many dissolved minerals that can interfere with your experimental work, you must work with water that is free of those impurities. Your laboratory will use either *distilled* or *deionized* water for those purposes. Throughout this laboratory manual, we will refer to distilled water; however, deionized water is just as suitable.

Since you will be using distilled water so frequently, you will find it helpful to have a polyethylene *wash bottle* that can be used for dispensing distilled water. Figure LE.9 shows two general types of wash bottles. The type in part (a) comes ready to use. If your laboratory equipment includes the type shown in part (b), you probably will be asked to prepare the glass portion in Experiment 2. Water may be dispensed from either type by squeezing the body of the bottle, and directing the stream of water as desired.

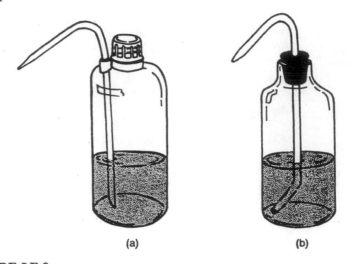

(a)   (b)

FIGURE LE.9
Polyethylene wash bottles. (a) Most wash bottles are purchased ready for use.
(b) Some wash bottles require construction of the glass spigot.

Since distilled water is more expensive than tap water, it is helpful if you do not waste it. The greatest waste of distilled water generally occurs during cleaning of glassware. To clean your equipment, use soap and tap water just as you would to clean your dishes at home: first clean with soap, and then rinse with tap water. After you have rinsed your glassware with tap water, use your wash bottle to rinse the surfaces of your glassware with distilled water. In the case of beakers, flasks, and test tubes, it is not necessary to fill the vessels with distilled water. Simply direct the stream of distilled water so that the tap water is rinsed from the sides of the glassware. Rinsing each piece of glassware twice with distilled water in this fashion will leave your equipment clean.

FILTRATION EQUIPMENT

It is often necessary to remove insoluble matter from the liquid or solution in which it is suspended. The liquid portion is referred to as the filtrate. The process of removing the insoluble matter from the filtrate is called *filtration*. There are two general methods of filtration: gravity filtration and vacuum filtration. Each method requires its own equipment.

Gravity Filtration Equipment
If you have ever made filtered coffee, you have already been introduced to the general technique of gravity filtration. To set up the necessary apparatus, support a long-stem funnel in an iron ring attached to a ring stand, as shown in Figure LE.10. Place an empty beaker or flask under the stem of the funnel to catch whatever liquids are poured through the funnel. Next, fold a piece of filter paper into quarters, and open it up to form a cone. Place the cone in the funnel and wet the filter paper with the solvent you are using. Water will be the solvent for most of the work described in this lab manual. Thus, your wash bottle filled with distilled water may be used conveniently for wetting the filter paper. Be sure that the filter paper is pressed against the walls of the funnel so that the water flows through the filter paper readily.

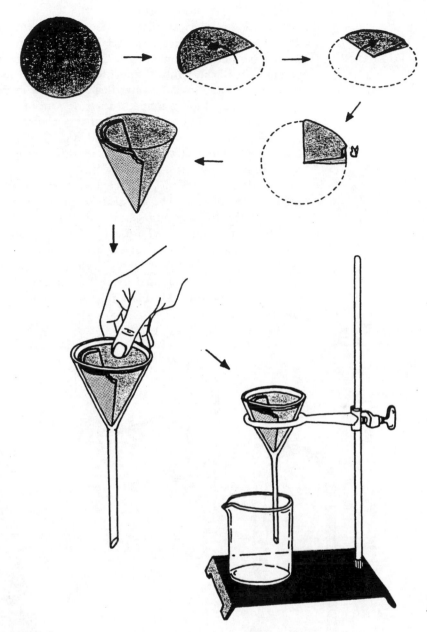

FIGURE LE.10
Apparatus for gravity filtration. The filter paper is folded into quarters to form a cone.

To filter the mixture to be separated, simply pour it through the funnel. The insoluble solids will remain in the filter, while the filtrate will come through. Some of the solids to be filtered may remain behind in the beaker or flask from which the mixture was poured. You may use your wash bottle to rinse these into the filter. If the substance you wish to collect is dissolved in the filtrate, some of it may remain soaked into the filter paper, which acts like a sponge. You may rinse the substance through the filter by washing the filter paper itself with a stream of distilled water.

Vacuum Filtration Equipment

Often it is necessary to filter a solid by a technique known as vacuum filtration. This technique requires a porcelain funnel, known as a Büchner funnel, and a filter flask that is designed so that suction may be applied to it (Fig. LE.11). To assemble a Büchner funnel and filter flask, the rubber stopper on the neck of the funnel is inserted into the filter flask as shown in figure LE.11. A piece of heavy-walled vacuum tubing connects the side arm of the filter flask to a device known as an *aspirator*, which is located on the laboratory faucet. The aspirator creates a suction when the spigot is turned on. The water flowing through the spigot does not flow out of the side arm of the aspirator, but instead creates a partial vacuum as it flows past the side arm.

After assembling the Büchner funnel and filter flask, place a piece of filter paper in the funnel. The diameter of the filter paper must match the inside diameter of the Büchner funnel so that the paper covers the bottom of the funnel and fits flat against it. To use the Büchner funnel, turn the spigot on and wet the filter paper with the solvent being used. The paper will be drawn tightly against the bottom of the funnel. Then pour the mixture to be filtered into the funnel. The suction created by the aspirator will draw the filtrate into the filter flask, while the insoluble material being filtered is left on the filter paper in the Büchner funnel.

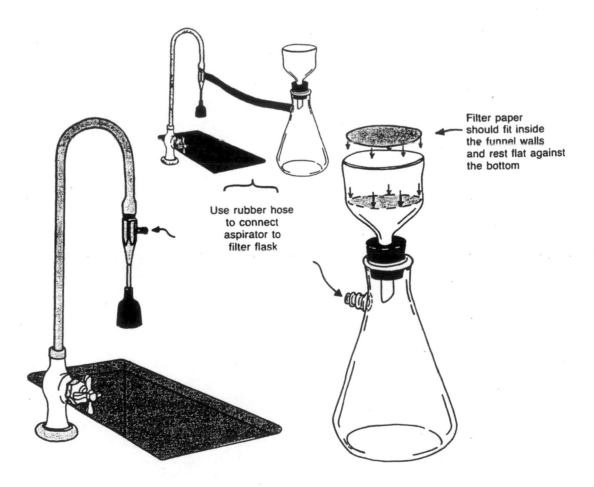

Filter paper should fit inside the funnel walls and rest flat against the bottom

Use rubber hose to connect aspirator to filter flask

FIGURE LE.11

Apparatus for vacuum filtration. A Büchner funnel and filter flask are connected to an aspirator. A circle of filter paper is inserted in the funnel.

TECHNIQUES FOR USING MISCELLANEOUS EQUIPMENT

Bunsen Burner and Glass Bending
The operation of the Bunsen burner and its use for bending glass is described in detail in Experiment 2.

Dispensing Chemicals from Bottles
It is important that you do not contaminate the chemicals you use when you dispense them. The following rules will prevent such contamination:

1. Always pour liquids from a bottle into a test tube, beaker, or flask for your own use. Never put a foreign eyedropper into any bottle. If a bottle has its own eyedropper, you may use it, but do not lay the dropper down on the lab bench or bring it into contact with other solutions.
2. To transfer a solid from a bottle, pour out an amount slightly greater than what you need into your own beaker. If you must use a spatula to dig a solid substance out of a bottle, be sure the spatula is clean and dry.
3. Never return unused chemicals to the bottle from which they were dispensed.

Pouring Corrosive Liquids
When liquids are to be transferred from a glass stoppered bottle, there is a natural tendency to remove the stopper and lay it on the laboratory bench. However, if this is done, the stopper may become contaminated by substances on the bench top. To prevent contamination, hold the stopper as shown in Figure LE.12. This method keeps the stopper from coming in contact with other substances and also requires the use of only one hand, leaving the other hand free. Always wear gloves when pouring corrosive liquids.

Occasionally, when liquids are poured freely, some splashing may occur. This can be dangerous if the liquid is corrosive, as is the case for acids and bases. To prevent splashing, hold a clean glass stirring rod as illustrated in Figure LE.13. The rod prevents splashing by guiding the liquid into the vessel.

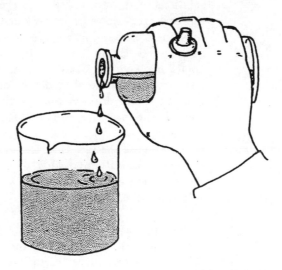

FIGURE LE.12
Holding a glass stopper. When pouring acids and bases, hold the glass stopper between your fingers to prevent contamination of the stopper.

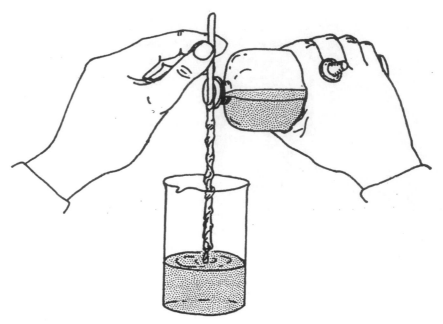

FIGURE LE.13
Pouring caustic liquids.   When pouring liquids, a stirring rod may be used to reduce splashing.

Disposal of Laboratory Wastes

During the past decade, environmental laws regulating the disposal of hazardous wastes have been significantly strengthened. As a result of this legislation, the appropriate disposal of laboratory wastes has become a complex matter that varies from state to state. Not all chemical wastes are considered *hazardous*, so some chemicals may be flushed down the drain. For example, sodium chloride (table salt) and calcium carbonate (marble) are not usually considered hazardous. Consequently, small volumes of these substances may be disposed of by rinsing solutions of them down the drain or, if they are in solid form, by placing them in the garbage. However, other chemicals, such as concentrated acids and bases or substances containing certain heavy metals, are considered a threat to human health and safety, and must therefore be disposed of in accordance with applicable Federal, State, and local regulations. Thus, it would be illegal and unethical to dispose of solutions or solids containing mercury or lead by pouring them down the drain or placing them in the garbage. Your instructor will advise you of the system used for the collection and disposal of wastes in your laboratory.

Despite the fact that the variation in environmental law from one locale to another makes it impossible to give specific rules for the disposal of laboratory wastes, there are certain "housekeeping" practices that you should follow, wherever your school is located:

1. Do not attempt to flush insoluble solids down the drain. In addition to "chemicals," insolubles include matches, paper towels, and litmus paper.
2. Never return unused chemicals to the bottles from which they were dispensed.
3. *If it is permitted in your locale*, always neutralize concentrated acids and bases before washing them down the drain. (The ability to dispose of many chemicals legally by flushing them down the drain depends on your school's sewer system.)

4. Your instructor will tell you how to dispose of the hazardous wastes and recyclable materials generated in each experiment you carry out.

Spill Cleanup Procedures

As mentioned in the "Laboratory Safety" section, spilled chemicals represent a safety hazard. In addition, they represent an environmental hazard, as improper cleanup procedures could result in the release of the chemicals to the environment. Your instructor will give you specific procedures for cleaning up spilled chemicals in your laboratory. However, the following general procedures may be applied to most situations.

1. Always wear rubber gloves when cleaning up a spilled chemical. It is very difficult to clean up a spill without coming in close contact with the spilled substance. Paper towels and other absorbent materials used in a cleanup may transfer chemicals to unprotected hands.

2. Neutralize concentrated acid spills by sprinkling enough baking soda (sodium hydrogen carbonate powder) on the spill to absorb all of the liquid. If the acid neutralized is hydrochloric acid, hydrobromic acid, nitric acid, sulfuric acid, or phosphoric acid, the solid generated is a nonhazardous solid that may be disposed of by washing down the drain. For other acids, dispose of the solid as a hazardous waste solid.

3. Neutralize concentrated base spills by sprinkling enough boric acid powder to absorb all of the liquid. Dispose of the solid with other hazardous waste solids.

4. For small amounts of aqueous solutions that contain only *nonhazardous* substances, use paper towels to soak up the liquid. Discard the paper towels in the garbage.

5. For small amounts of aqueous solutions that contain hazardous substances, use paper towels to soak up the liquid. Discard the paper towels as a hazardous waste solid.

6. For large amounts of liquids that contain hazardous substances, use a spill pillow or vermiculite to absorb the spill. Dispose of the contaminated absorbent as a hazardous waste solid. Always get help when handling larger spills.

7. For spilled solids, sweep up the solid and place it in the appropriate waste container. For nonhazardous solids (such as sodium bicarbonate), the solid may be placed in the garbage. Place hazardous solids in the appropriate hazardous waste solid container.

8. Following initial cleanup of the spill, wash the affected surfaces with water. Any towels or rags used for this final "touch-up" may be disposed of in the garbage.

ILLUSTRATIONS OF COMMON LABORATORY EQUIPMENT

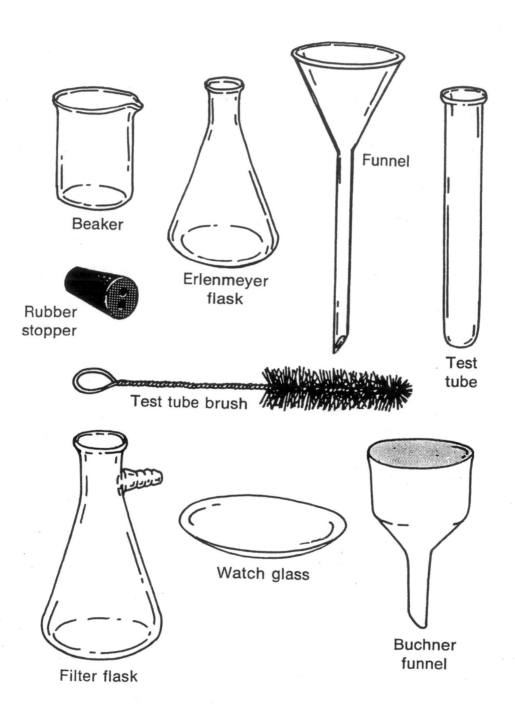

Beaker

Rubber stopper

Erlenmeyer flask

Funnel

Test tube

Test tube brush

Filter flask

Watch glass

Buchner funnel

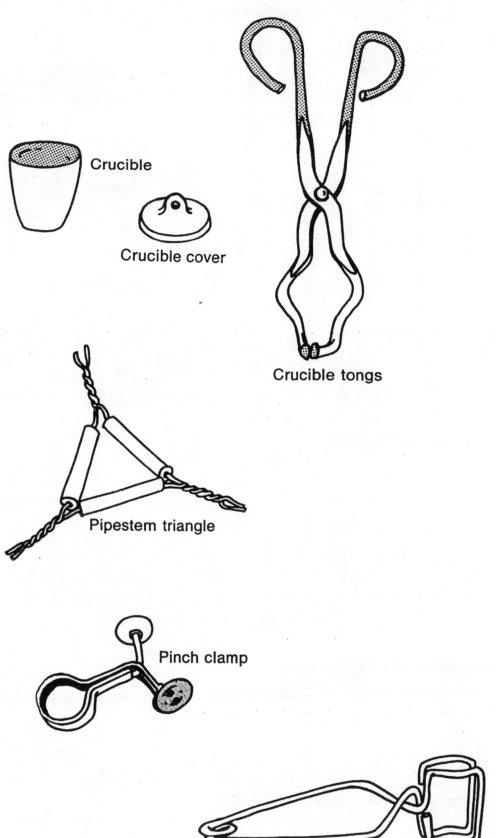

Crucible

Crucible cover

Crucible tongs

Pipestem triangle

Pinch clamp

Test tube holder

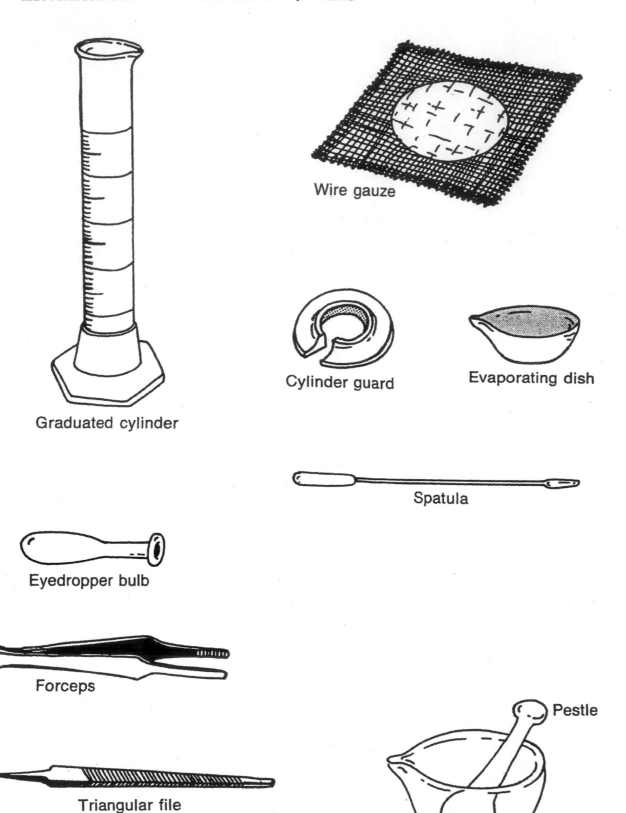

Graduated cylinder

Wire gauze

Cylinder guard

Evaporating dish

Spatula

Eyedropper bulb

Forceps

Triangular file

Pestle

Mortar

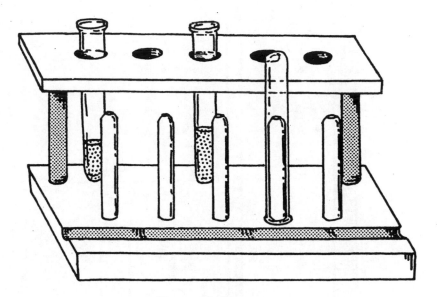

Test tube rack

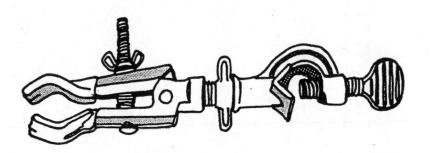

Universal clamp

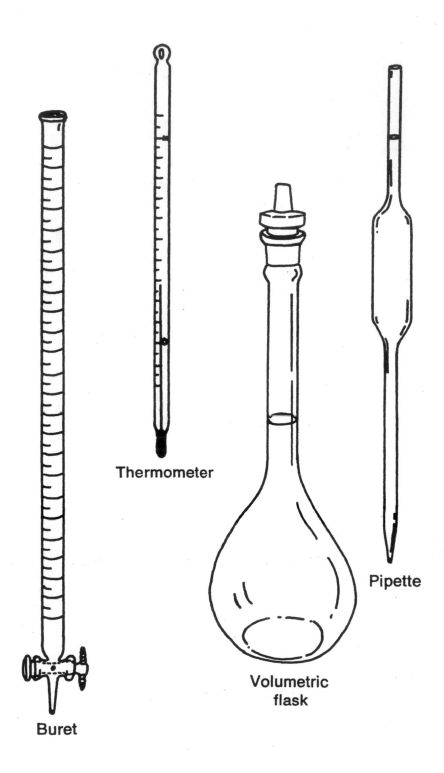

Thermometer

Pipette

Volumetric
flask

Buret

TECH
600

modular · laboratory · program · in · chemistry

publisher: H. A. Neidig   editor: M. L. Gillette

Practicing Safety in the Chemistry Laboratory

prepared by **M. L. Gillette**, Indiana University Kokomo; **H. A. Neidig**, Lebanon Valley College; and **J. N. Spencer**, Franklin and Marshall College

Purpose of the Exercise

Learn behaviors that promote safe laboratory experiences. Sign a safety agreement confirming your promise to follow safe practices in the laboratory.

Background Information

Your awareness of potential hazards and your respectful approach to the work you are going to perform are both essential to your safety in the chemistry laboratory. In addition, each person's safety in the laboratory depends on the responsible behavior of everyone else present.

The frequency of laboratory accidents can be sharply reduced if everyone follows all of the safety precautions and directions given for each experiment. In general, remember these three basic rules:

- Read the entire experiment before coming to the laboratory.

- Follow established procedures when working with laboratory materials and apparatus.

- Know how to get help if an accident does occur.

Safe Laboratory Practices

1. Wear departmentally approved safety goggles at all times.

Always wear departmentally approved safety goggles in the chemistry laboratory, regardless of any corrective eyewear you may require. Contact lenses may be worn in most laboratory environments, provided that approved safety goggles are also worn. However, contact lenses may not be worn in areas where you may be exposed to certain OSHA-regulated substances. Your laboratory instructor will advise you when contact lenses are not permitted.

2. Know the exact location and operation of all safety equipment in the laboratory.

Your laboratory instructor will identify the locations and explain the procedures for using the eyewash fountain(s), safety shower(s), fire alarm, fire blanket(s), fire extinguisher(s), fire pail(s), material safety data sheets, and first aid station(s). Your laboratory instructor will also point out the telephone and the emergency exit nearest to your laboratory bench. Learn the locations and policies for uses of these items—your safety depends on them.

Complete the **Safety Information** section later in this module.

3. *Never* work alone in the laboratory.

A laboratory instructor will always be present during an assigned laboratory period. If you encounter any difficulties, the instructor will be available to assist you. *Never* begin or continue any laboratory work without an instructor being present.

4. Do only the experiment assigned by your laboratory instructor.

Never do unauthorized work in the laboratory. In addition, do not alter the designated experimental procedure without your instructor's permission.

5. Wear protective clothing.

To protect your feet and legs from spilled chemicals, broken glass, or falling apparatus, do not wear open-toed shoes or sandals, and make sure that your legs are covered. Do not wear clothing with loose sleeves. Your laboratory instructor may ask or require you to protect your clothing by wearing a nonflammable, nonporous laboratory apron or a laboratory coat. Tie back long hair so that it will not fall into flames or chemicals, or become caught in equipment or machinery.

6. Keep the laboratory bench and floor around your work area uncluttered.

Place such items as purses, bookbags, coats, and books in designated areas, not on the laboratory bench or on the floor around your work area. Place only authorized materials, such as laboratory instructions, a notebook, and a pen or pencils, on your laboratory bench.

7. *Never* eat, drink, use tobacco, or apply lip balm in the laboratory.

To avoid contact with toxic substances, either airborne or spilled on the laboratory bench, *never* bring food or cigarettes into the laboratory. *Never* drink from laboratory glassware, because it might be contaminated. Keep your hands away from your face and mouth.

8. Come prepared, and use good judgment and care when working in the laboratory.

Carefully read the entire experiment before you come to the laboratory. Make sure that you understand all cautions about potential hazards and all warnings concerning critical steps in the procedure. Report to the laboratory on time, so as not to miss any important instructions from your laboratory instructor.

Do not use cracked or chipped glassware. Replace it with undamaged glassware.

Never taste any chemical in the laboratory.

Avoid inhaling fumes of any kind. If you are directed to detect an odor in an experiment, gently waft the vapors toward your nose with a cupped hand, or use the method recommended by your laboratory instructor. *Never* put your face directly over a container, such as a test tube, and directly inhale vapors.

Inform your instructor of any allergies or medical conditions you have that might affect your performance in the laboratory.

9. Read reagent bottle and container labels *carefully*.

Make certain that you are using the appropriate chemicals and solutions for the experiment. Before you transfer a chemical or solution from a reagent bottle, carefully read the label. Record the identity of the reagent and, if appropriate, its concentration on your Data and Observations sheet or in your laboratory notebook. To ensure accurate identification of the reagent, read the label again before you put the container back on the shelf.

Figure 1 *A typical NFPA hazard label*

Be sure to note whether or not there is a National Fire Protection Association (NFPA) diamond-shaped hazard label on the reagent bottle. A typical NFPA label is shown in Figure 1. These labels list the NFPA hazard ratings for the substance in the bottle, including any personal protection required when using the reagent. The ratings run from 0 to 4, representing least to most hazardous, respectively.

Never pour unused reagents back into the reagent bottle. Instead, dispose of leftover reagents as directed by your laboratory instructor.

Material safety data sheets (MSDS) for all chemicals used in a laboratory must be on file at a location known to the laboratory instructor. Federal law requires that chemical suppliers make the MSDS information available to users of these chemicals. The first section of an MSDS usually lists all the names by which the chemical is known, its chemical formula, supplier's name, and, if applicable, the NFPA hazard ratings. The remaining sections may include such information as physical data, fire and explosion hazards, reactivity data, health hazards, spills and disposal procedures, special protection information, and storage and handling procedures. MSDS vary, from supplier to supplier, in terms of their exact layout and contents. Part of a typical MSDS for acetone is shown in Figure 2 on the next page.

10. Avoid burns from hot objects.

When you heat a chemical in a container, the burner (or hot plate) and the clamp holding the container also get hot. Do not touch hot objects. Do not place hot objects directly on the laboratory bench or a towel. Instead, use tongs to place hot objects on a heat-resistant mat or board.

11. Use a fume hood when you are directed to do so.

Fume hoods safely remove toxic, irritating, and flammable vapors from the laboratory.

12. *Immediately* report *all* injuries, no matter how minor, to your laboratory instructor.

Your laboratory instructor will help treat any injuries and keep a written record of all accidents that occur in the laboratory.

13. Dispose of used materials according to your laboratory instructor's directions.

For the safety of the people who process discarded materials, dispose of all materials in properly marked containers.

14. Help keep the laboratory clean at all times.

Clean up any spilled chemicals in the area around the balances and on the laboratory bench. Before you leave the laboratory, wipe the bench top thoroughly, and properly dispose of burned matches and paper scraps.

15. Wash your hands thoroughly before you leave the laboratory.

Before you leave the laboratory, wash your hands thoroughly with soap or detergent to remove all traces of reagents from your skin.

If an Accident Does Occur

In spite of the best efforts of all concerned, laboratory accidents do occur. Consequently, you must know what to do in response to particular situations.

The following examples illustrate some of the more common types of accidents that occur. Your laboratory instructor will elaborate on the general information presented here. In addition, your instructor may suggest modifications of these procedures that will make them more appropriate for your laboratory.

MATERIAL SAFETY DATA SHEET

Section 1. IDENTITY

		NFPA Hazard Rating	
Name	**ACETONE**		
Synonyms	**2-PROPANONE, DIMETHYLKETONE**	health	1
Formula	$CH_3C(O)CH_3$	flammability	3
RTECS No.	**AL3150000**	reactivity	0
CAS No.	**67-64-1**		

Section 2. HAZARDOUS COMPONENTS

Component	%	TLV
ACETONE	100	1000 ppm (2375 mg/m^3)

Section 3. PHYSICAL DATA

Clear, colorless, volatile liquid with a characteristic mint-like odor. Soluble in alcohol, ether, benzene, chloroform, most dimethylformamides, and oils.

Boiling point: 133 °F (56 °C).   Specific Gravity: 0.7899
Volatility: 100%   Vapor pressure: 180 mm Hg @ 20 °C

Section 4. FIRE, EXPLOSION HAZARDS

Dangerous fire hazard when exposed to heat or flame. Vapors are heavier than air and may travel a considerable distance to source of ignition.

Flash point: −4 °F (−20 °C).

Section 5. HEALTH HAZARDS

Inhalation: Irritant and narcotic. 20,000 ppm immediately dangerous to life.

Section 6. STORAGE AND HANDLING

Observe all Federal, state, and local regulations when storing or disposing of this substance. For assistance, contact the district director of the Environmental Protection Agency.
STORAGE: Store in accordance with 29 CFR 1910.106. Bonding and grounding: Substance with low electroconductivity that may be ignited by electrostatic sparks should be stored in containers that meet the bonding and grounding guidelines specified in NFPA 77-1983. Store away from incompatible substances.

Section 7. SPILLS AND DISPOSAL

Disposal must be in accordance with standards applicable to generators of hazardous waste; see 40 CFR 262. EPA hazardous waste number U002. Occupational spill: Shut off ignition sources. Stop leak if you can do so without risk. Use water spray to reduce vapors. For small spills, take up with sand or other absorbent material, and place into containers for later disposal.

Figure 2 *A partial MSDS for acetone, showing a typical MSDS format*

Burns *Immediately* notify your laboratory instructor about any burn. Burns from hot objects, flames, or chemicals should all be treated in the same way: Flush the affected area with cool, running water for 20 minutes. Your instructor will determine whether or not the burn should receive medical attention.

Cuts and Wounds *Immediately* notify your laboratory instructor about any cut or wound you receive in the laboratory. All such wounds should be considered serious and treated carefully. Your instructor will determine what kind of medical care is needed.

Chemical Spills on the Laboratory Bench, Reagent Shelf, or Floor *Immediately* notify your bench neighbors and your laboratory instructor about any spill and the substances involved. Clean up the spill as directed by your laboratory instructor.

If the spill involves volatile, flammable materials, tell everyone in the laboratory to extinguish all flames. Disconnect any spark-producing equipment. Shut down all experiments. Evacuate the laboratory, if your laboratory instructor tells you to do so.

Chemical Spills on a Person

Over a Large Area

Immediately notify your laboratory instructor about any large spill on a person. Your instructor might take one or both of the following actions, depending on the extent and location of the spill:

Using the safety shower, flood the affected body area with cold water for at least 20 minutes. Quickly remove all contaminated clothing while the person is under the shower.

Wash off chemicals using a mild detergent solution. Rinse the affected area with cold water.

In either case, your laboratory instructor will obtain medical assistance immediately.

Over a Small Area

Immediately flush the area thoroughly with cold water. Notify your laboratory instructor, who will take any appropriate further action.

In the Eyes

Immediately call for assistance in getting to the nearest eyewash fountain. Drench your eyes for at least 20 minutes, carefully holding them wide open. Rotate your eyeballs in order to flush all areas. Meanwhile, your laboratory instructor will obtain the necessary medical assistance.

If a chemical splashes on your face while you are wearing safety goggles, **keep the goggles on**. If you remove the goggles immediately following such a spill, the splashed chemical may get into your eyes. Instead, *immediately* get to the nearest eyewash fountain, and drench your face and goggles. When you have completely rinsed the chemical from your face and goggles, remove the goggles. Then proceed to drench your eyes for at least 20 minutes, as described above.

Ingesting Chemicals

Immediately notify your laboratory instructor if you accidentally ingest a chemical. Your instructor will take appropriate action for the specific substance ingested.

Unconsciousness

Inhalation of, or skin contact with, certain chemicals can cause respiratory failure, resulting in unconsciousness. Electric shock can have the same effect. If anyone becomes unconscious in the laboratory, *immediately* call for your laboratory instructor.

Fire

Immediately alert the proper authorities about any fire and its status. Call for additional assistance, if needed. In the case of a major fire, go to a safe area agreed upon by the emergency responders, and wait there to direct them to the fire.

If your clothing is burning, *immediately* move away from the source of the fire and **stop–drop–roll: Stop** what you are doing, **drop** to the floor, and **roll** over and over to extinguish the flames. **Call for help**. Keep rolling until someone else gets a fire blanket to help smother the flames on your clothing.

If your clothing is burning, **do not run** to the fire blanket or safety shower. Running fans the flames, increasing your chances of sustaining respiratory damage from inhalation of hot, toxic fumes.

If someone else's clothing catches fire, *immediately* move the person away from the source of the fire. Make them **stop–drop–roll**. Use the fire blanket to help smother the flames. *Immediately* call for your laboratory instructor. Remove the fire blanket as soon as the flames have been extinguished, so that the victim will not be burned further by hot clothing.

While the victim is being cared for, other people should try to shut off or at least reduce the fuel supply to the fire, unless your laboratory instructor has told you to evacuate the laboratory. If the fire is small, and you have experience in doing so and are confident of success, control and extinguish the fire by directing the spray of an appropriate fire extinguisher at the **base** of the fire.

Safety Information

The safety information presented here applies to any chemistry laboratory. Therefore, make yourself thoroughly familiar with it. Many experiments also contain additional warnings about steps or reagents that may be hazardous. For this reason, it is important that you read the entire experiment before you attempt to carry out the procedure.

Be especially aware of the safety resources in your laboratory. The safety equipment and related facilities usually found in a typical chemistry laboratory are listed below. Next to each item, record its location in your laboratory. There is also room to record important telephone numbers and additional safety instructions that your laboratory instructor may give you. In an emergency, this information will help you to quickly take the correct action. A few seconds saved can mean the difference between severe injury or damage and a minor inconvenience.

When you have finished recording all the safety information, ask your laboratory instructor to sign and date this page. Make sure you have this page with you whenever you are working in the laboratory.

Location of Safety Resources

eyewash fountain: **nearest emergency exit:**

safety shower: **fire extinguisher:**

first aid station: **fire blanket:**

material safety data sheets: **nearest telephone:**

fire alarm: **fire pail:**

Emergency Telephone Numbers

fire: **poison center:**   **police:**

Additional Safety Instructions

_____   _____
student's signature   date

_____   _____
laboratory instructor's signature   date

Carefully read the following **Chemistry Laboratory Safety Agreement**. Once you have read and understood the Agreement, you must sign it. Then you must ask your laboratory instructor to sign it.

Chemistry Laboratory Safety Agreement

Any time I am working in, or even visiting, the laboratory, I will follow the laboratory safety practices recommended in this module, and I will take the following precautions:

1. Wear departmentally approved safety goggles at all times.

2. Know the exact location and operation of all safety equipment in the laboratory.

3. *Never* work alone in the laboratory.

4. Do only the experiment assigned by my laboratory instructor.

5. Wear protective clothing.

6. Keep the laboratory bench and floor around my work area uncluttered.

7. *Never* eat, drink, use tobacco, or apply lip balm in the laboratory.

8. Come prepared, and use good judgment and care when I work in the laboratory.

9. Read reagent bottle and container labels *carefully.*

10. Avoid burns from hot objects.

11. Use a fume hood when I am directed to do so.

12. *Immediately* report *all* injuries, no matter how minor, to my laboratory instructor.

13. Dispose of used materials according to my laboratory instructor's directions.

14. Help keep the laboratory clean at all times.

15. Wash my hands thoroughly before I leave the laboratory.

I have carefully read the discussion of recommended laboratory safety practices and the precautions listed above. I understand my role in protecting the safety of everyone in the laboratory. I agree to follow these practices and take these precautions whenever I am in the laboratory.

_____   _____
student's signature   date

_____   _____   _____   _____
course   section   locker number   room number

_____   _____
laboratory instructor's signature   date

Laboratory Safety Quiz

1. Why is it important to tie back long hair when working in the laboratory?

2. Why should you never bring food into the laboratory?

3. What should you do if you spill a flammable liquid on your laboratory bench?

4. Why is it dangerous to wear open-toed shoes or sandals in the laboratory?

5. What procedure should you follow if a liquid splashes in your face while you are wearing safety goggles?

6. List the poor judgments and safety violations made by Thomas and his laboratory partner in the following scenario.

Thomas arrived a few minutes late for laboratory because he had been trying to find his syllabus, in order to determine which experiment he was scheduled to do. In his hurry, he had forgotten his safety goggles. He hoped his instructor would not notice. After unpacking his bookbag on the laboratory bench, Thomas discovered a half-eaten candy bar, which he put aside to finish later in the laboratory period. After Thomas and his partner started their experiment, they noticed a big crack in the beaker they were using. Because they were rushing to catch up with the rest of the class, they decided to continue with the experiment, which involved heating a solution in the beaker. The beaker broke, spilling a hot, corrosive solution on the laboratory bench. The solution ran onto the floor and Thomas's sandals, splashing his feet with hot, corrosive liquid. So as not to call attention to their problems, Thomas continued the experiment, using a different beaker, while his partner tossed the pieces of the broken beaker into a basket marked 'paper only'. That night, Thomas was unable to sleep because the burns on his feet, although superficial, were very painful.

EXPERIMENT
2

The Bunsen Burner
and Glass Working

PURPOSE

1. To understand the function and operation of the Bunsen burner.
2. To develop proficiency in cutting and bending of glass tubing.
3. To prepare items of equipment for laboratory use.

DISCUSSION

I. The Bunsen Burner

The Bunsen burner uses natural gas, which is composed primarily of methane (CH_4). Methane is a gas at room temperature, and its complete combustion with oxygen produces carbon dioxide and water vapor:

$$CH_4 + 2\ O_2 \rightarrow CO_2 + 2\ H_2O$$

If insufficient oxygen is present, carbon monoxide or carbon may be produced:

$$2\ CH_4 + 3\ O_2 \rightarrow 2\ CO + 4\ H_2O$$

$$CH_4 + O_2 \rightarrow C + 2\ H_2O$$

Bunsen burners vary in their design, but all Bunsen burners have certain features in common (Fig. 2.1). Natural gas is generally introduced into the *base* through a rubber tube that leads from the gas supply valve on the laboratory bench. The gas then passes into a chamber called the *barrel*, in which gas and oxygen are mixed. Attached to the bottom of the barrel are *air ports* that may be adjusted to increase or decrease the amount of oxygen mixed with the natural gas. If the mixture contains insufficient oxygen to burn the natural gas completely, a yellow flame results. This is referred to as a *luminous* flame. When combustion is complete, the flame is blue. We call this the *nonluminous* flame. A luminous flame may be made nonluminous by adjusting the air ports to increase the ratio of oxygen to natural gas.

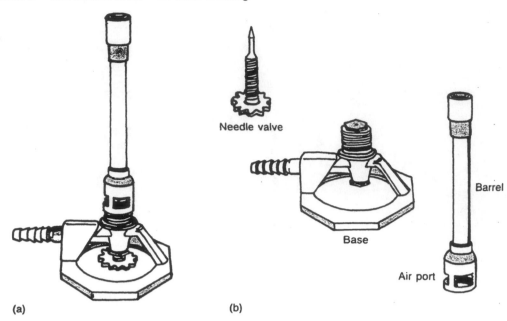

Needle valve

Base

Barrel

Air port

(a)   (b)

FIGURE 2.1
Bunsen burner: (a) assembled, (b) disassembled.

II.   Glass Working

It is often necessary to make different pieces of glass apparatus for use in experimental work. Therefore, you will be given some experience in cutting, fire polishing, bending, and drawing out glass tubing. You will use your Bunsen burner to accomplish this.

Glass tubing and glass rod can be broken cleanly with the help of a file. When this is done, the newly exposed ends of the glass are sharp and may cut you if they are not made smooth. This is done by a technique known as *fire polishing*. Sharp edges are fire polished by heating the glass in the Bunsen burner until the glass becomes soft, thereby rounding the sharp edges. When fire polishing glass tubing, be careful not to heat the glass for too long, or the ends will seal shut. You will prepare several stirring rods from a solid glass rod by simply fire polishing the broken ends.

Glass tubing may be bent at angles by heating the glass in a flame until it becomes soft. Once the glass softens, it may be bent to the desired angle. If this process is carried out in the normal flame of your Bunsen burner, however, the bend in the glass will be constricted, like a garden hose that has been bent over on itself. To avoid such a constriction, the flame must be spread using a special adaptor known as a *wing top* or *flame spreader*. You will be asked to prepare several bends using your wing top. You will also be asked to prepare several eyedroppers by drawing out the end of a piece of glass tubing into a fine capillary tip. Your instructor will demonstrate the techniques you will be expected to learn.

PRELAB QUESTIONS

1. What is the purpose of fire polishing glass? Why is it inadvisable to try to fire polish the tips of the eyedroppers you make?
2. What are the products of complete combustion of natural gas?
3. How is glass tubing broken in two?

EXPERIMENTAL

Materials

6 mm soft glass tubing
4 mm glass rod
Bunsen burner (with wing top and rubber connecting hose)
triangular file
wire gauze
crucible tongs
150 mL beaker
evaporating dish
two rubber bulbs for eyedroppers
10 mL graduated cylinder
polyethylene bottle fitted with one-hole stopper (optional)
iron ring
ring stand

Time Required

2 to 3 hours

Cleaning Up

General instructions for disposing of wastes generated in this experiment are provided at the end of each experimental procedure. Additional, more specific information and suggestions for managing any hazardous wastes may be found in the *Instructor's Guide*. Your instructor will provide you with special waste handling directions when necessary.

PROCEDURE

I. The Bunsen Burner

1. Examine each part of your Bunsen burner (Fig. 2.1). If your Bunsen burner can be disassembled easily, do so. Identify the base, the air ports, and the barrel. If you have taken your burner apart, reassemble it. Be sure you understand how to open and close the air ports. Check to see that you know how to attach and remove the wing top from the top of the barrel. What is the function of each part of the burner?

2. Connect the hose to the gas outlet on your laboratory bench. With the air ports closed all the way, hold a lighted match over the burner, and open the gas valve to light the burner. Open the valve slowly, or its draft may blow out the match before the burner is lit. Control the gas flow at the gas valve (or at the needle valve if your Bunsen burner has one). Slowly open the air ports. Note the changes in the appearance of the flame as the air ports are opened and closed. Describe the flame as either luminous (yellow) or nonluminous (blue) with the air ports opened and closed. When the nonluminous flame is adjusted properly, you will observe an inner cone within the flame itself. Be sure you can adjust the flame in this fashion.

3. Connect an iron ring to a ring stand, and place a piece of wire gauze on it. Next, place a beaker containing cold water on the wire gauze and dash the flame of your lighted burner across the side of the beaker. Note anything that happens to the beaker as this is done. Record your observations.

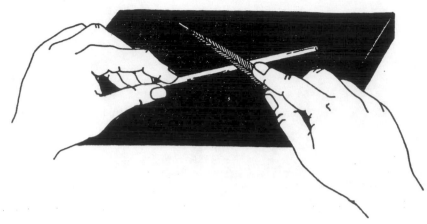

FIGURE 2.2
*Scoring glass tubing. Hold tubing on a bench while making a scratch
with a triangular file.*

4. Hold a cold evaporating dish in the luminous flame with your crucible tongs
   for about a minute and observe what happens. Next, produce a nonluminous flame and hold the same evaporating dish over it for a few minutes.
   Record your observations.
5. Use your wire gauze to determine the relative temperatures of the various
   parts of a nonluminous flame. When the wire gauze becomes hot, it will
   have a red glow. Begin by placing a corner of the gauze in the middle of
   the lower cone. Observe the colors of the gauze to determine the hottest
   parts of this portion of the flame. Next, put the gauze just at the top of the
   inner cone. Finally, place the gauze at the top of the flame. Sketch the
   parts of the flame, and record all of your observations on the sketch. Use
   your observations to label the hottest and coldest part of the flame.

II. Glass Working

Read the following discussion of glass working techniques before making any of
the equipment described.

Breaking Tubing or Rod.   Glass tubes and rods up to about 8 mm or 10 mm in
diameter can be broken cleanly with the help of a file. Simply lay the piece of

File scratch

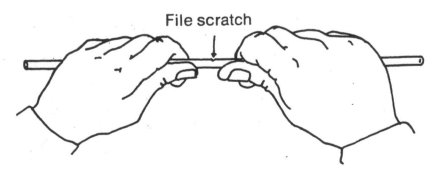

FIGURE 2.3
Applying pressure to break glass cleanly.

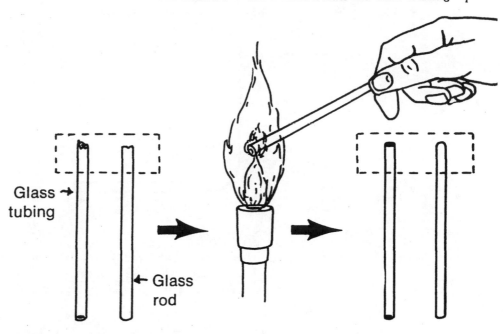

FIGURE 2.4
Fire polishing glass tubing and glass rod.

tubing on a bench top, hold it firmly with one hand, and draw the edge of a triangular file firmly across the tubing to score (scratch) the glass at the point at which the desired break is to be made (Fig. 2.2). (It is only necessary to score the glass once in this fashion.) Then rotate the glass tubing and place your thumbs on the side opposite the scratch. The application of a little pressure normally results in a clean break (Fig. 2.3).

Fire Polishing. After glass tubing has been cut, the edges are sharp and can cut your skin, even if the break is perfectly clean. To remove these sharp edges, hold the newly cut ends of the tubing in the hottest part of the flame and rotate the glass until it softens and flows sufficiently to round the sharp edges (Fig. 2.4). (PRECAUTION: Be very careful when working with hot glass. Hot glass

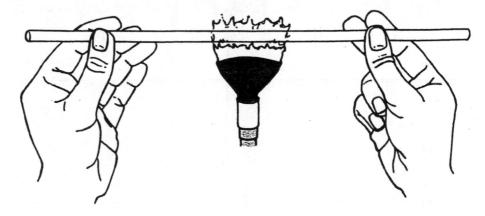

FIGURE 2.5
Using the wing top. Rotate glass tubing just above the blue inner part of the flame before removing it from the flame and bending.

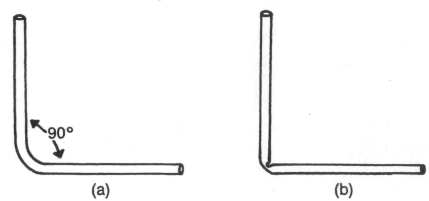

FIGURE 2.6
*Ninety-degree bend. (a) A properly made bend allows liquids and gases to
flow without restriction. (b) The glass in an improperly made bend is constricted, restricting the flow of liquids and gases.*

and cold glass may *look* the same, but they *feel* very different! Do not place hot
glass directly on the bench top. Instead, place it on a piece of wire gauze.)

Bending Glass Tubing.   To make bends in glass tubing, first you must spread
the flame of the burner with a wing top. Hold the glass tubing in both hands
with the part to be bent just above the blue area of the flame (Fig. 2.5). Rotate
the tubing slowly in the flame until the glass begins to soften and sag a little.
Take it out of the flame and bend it to the desired angle without allowing the
glass to cool. While making the bend, take care to hold the glass so it will lie
in a single plane. Figure 2.6 shows two 90° bends. Figure 2.6a illustrates how the
tubing should look when the bend has been made properly. If a wing top is not

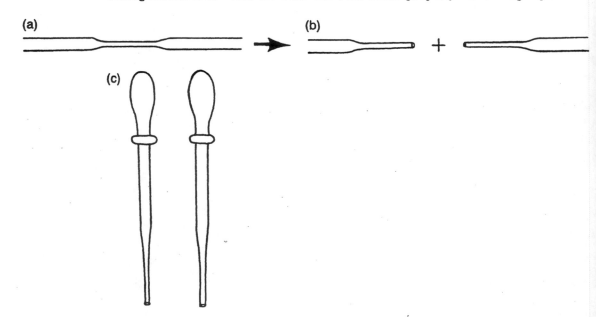

FIGURE 2.7
*Drawing glass into eyedroppers. After heating a piece of glass tubing with the
wing top, (a) draw it out, and (b) cut it in half. (c) Each piece may be used as
an eyedropper.*

used, the bend may be constricted like the one shown in Figure 2.6b. The constriction formed by the lump of glass on the inside of the bend reduces the flow of gas or liquid through the tubing. To avoid such constrictions, always use a wing top for bending glass tubing.

Drawing Tubing. Tubing may be drawn out into fine capillary tubing by heating the glass until it softens and then drawing it out like taffy. This may be done with or without the wing top. You may wish to try it both ways to see which gives you the better results. (To remove a hot wing top from your Bunsen burner, turn the gas off and allow the wing top to cool before removing it.) To draw out a piece of tubing, hold the middle of the glass tubing in the hottest portion of the flame while rotating the tube until the glass starts to soften and begins to sag slightly. Take the tube out of the flame, hold both ends firmly, pull the ends apart slowly. If the glass has been softened properly, it will be drawn out easily, producing a thin tube with very thin walls (Fig. 2.7a). When the glass has cooled, it can be cut at an appropriate spot to make an eyedropper, or two (Fig. 2.7b). A rubber bulb slipped over the large end of the tube will complete the eyedropper construction (Fig. 2.7c).

Practice fire polishing, bending, and drawing glass by making the pieces of equipment shown in Figure 2.8 as follows:

1. Make two stirring rods from 4 mm glass rod. To make each stirring rod, cut a piece of glass about 20 cm long, and fire polish both ends.

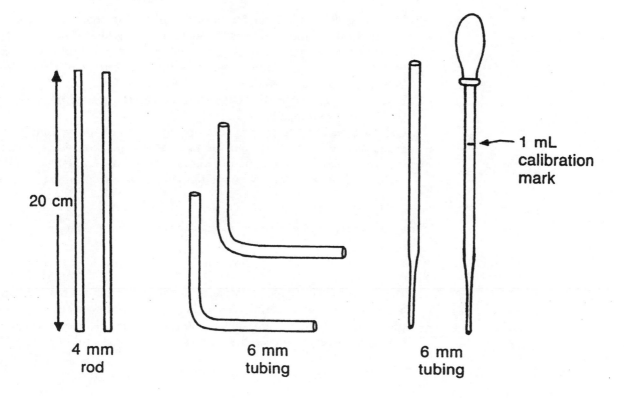

20 cm

4 mm
rod

6 mm
tubing

6 mm
tubing

1 mL
calibration
mark

FIGURE 2.8
Equipment inventory. Prepare two stirring rods, two right angle bends, and two eyedroppers.

2. Make two 90° bends from 5 mm or 6 mm tubing. For each piece, cut a 25 cm length of tubing, and bend the glass in the middle. Fire polish the ends.

3. Make two eyedroppers from 6 mm tubing. Cut a 25 cm length of tubing, heat the glass in the middle, and draw the glass out. Cut the capillary portion at a place that will give you a usable eyedropper. If you are lucky, both halves can be used. Otherwise, repeat the procedure until you have two usable eyedroppers.

4. Calibrate each eyedropper by drawing up 1 mL of water from your 10 mL graduated cylinder. Use your file to scratch a mark on each eyedropper at the 1 mL mark. Determine the number of drops of water per milliliter for each eye dropper. Then calculate the volume per drop for each.

Show your completed equipment to your instructor for grading.

Cleaning Up

Dispose of all unusable glass pieces as directed. Your laboratory may have a special disposal container for broken glass. If so, dispose of all unusable pieces of glass in this container. Return all usable pieces of glass to the location where you obtained your glass rod and glass tubing.

EXPERIMENT
3

Measurement

PURPOSE

1. To develop some proficiency in the use of metric units.
2. To become familiar with some of the common measuring devises used in a chemistry laboratory.
3. To learn about precision and accuracy in making measurements.

DISCUSSION

Scientific work often involves measurements. Most scientific measurements are carried out using metric units, such as those found in the International System (SI). Metric units for the same type of measurement are related to one another by powers of 10. For example, 1.25 meters is equal to 125 centimeters. Similarly, 2.5 kilograms is equal to 2500 grams. These simple decimal relationships make conversion from one unit to another quite simple.

Although the International System has been universally adopted for scientific work, it is generally not used for nonscientific measurements in the United States. In this experiment, you will become familiar with the units of measurement you will be using most frequently in your laboratory work. These include units of length, volume, and mass. In addition, you will work with density, a quantity that describes the ratio of mass to volume for a particular substance.

In this experiment, you will learn how to use several pieces of laboratory equipment. If you have not previously read "Laboratory Equipment," you should read the portions of that section that pertain to mass measurement and volume measurement before beginning the experiment. Those discussions will instruct you in the proper use of balances and techniques for using volumetric equipment.

I. Length

The meter (m) is the basic SI unit of length. Associated with it are the kilometer (km), centimeter (cm), and millimeter (mm). These units are related to one another as follows:

$$1000 \text{ m} = 1 \text{ km}$$

$$1 \text{ m} = 100 \text{ cm}$$

$$1 \text{ m} = 1000 \text{ mm}$$

Lengths in the International System may be related to English units of length. The following are useful equivalences between the two systems:

$$1 \text{ in.} = 2.54 \text{ cm}$$

$$1 \text{ km} = 0.621 \text{ mi}$$

$$1 \text{ m} = 1.09 \text{ yd}$$

Notice that the meter itself is slightly more than 1 yard.

II. Temperature

Laboratory measurement of temperature is generally done using the Celsius temperature scale (°C). SI temperatures are expressed using the Kelvin scale (K). These two temperature scales are related by the following equation:

$$T_K = T_C + 273$$

The Celsius scale is also related to the Fahrenheit scale:

$$T_F = (1.8)T_C + 32$$

Thus, a room temperature of 68°F corresponds to 20°C.

$$68 = (1.8)T_C + 32$$

$$T_C = \frac{(68 - 32)}{1.8} = \frac{36}{1.8} = 20°C$$

This corresponds to 293 K:

$$T_K = 20 + 273 = 293 \text{ K}$$

III. Volume

The basic unit of volume used in the chemistry laboratory is the liter (L). Related to the liter is the milliliter (mL), which is one-thousandth of a liter (0.001 L). Thus, there are 1000 milliliters in a liter. A milliliter is equal to the volume of a cube that measures 1 cm on each side. Since the volume of a cube is equal to its length times its width times its height, the volume of a cube that measures 1 cm on each side is equal to 1 cm^3. The following relationships commonly are used to relate metric units of volume:

$$1 \text{ L} = 1000 \text{ mL} = 1000 \text{ cm}^3$$

$$1 \text{ mL} = 1 \text{ cm}^3$$

The liter is slightly larger than the quart:

$$946 \text{ mL} = 1 \text{ qt}$$

IV. Mass

The kilogram (kg) is the SI unit of mass. It is equal to 1000 grams (g). The gram may be further subdivided into 1000 milligrams (mg):

$$1 \text{ kg} = 1000 \text{ g}$$

$$1 \text{ g} = 1000 \text{ mg}$$

These units are related to the English unit of mass, the pound, as follows:

$$1 \text{ lb} = 454 \text{ g}$$

$$1 \text{ kg} = 2.20 \text{ lb}$$

Mass and weight are not the same. Mass is a quantity of matter. Weight refers to the gravitational force of attraction exerted upon an object. In the laboratory, we will only be concerned with mass measurement. Nevertheless, the verb *weigh* will be used to mean *determine the mass of.*

V. Density

The density of a substance is its mass per unit volume:

$$d = \frac{m}{V}$$

where d is the symbol for density, m = mass, and V = volume. The density of a liquid that has a mass of 384 g and a volume of 48.0 mL is 8.00 g/mL:

$$d = \frac{m}{V} = \frac{384 \text{ g}}{48.0 \text{ mL}} = 8.00 \text{ g/mL}$$

The density of a liquid can be determined readily by measuring both the mass and volume of the same sample. In scientific work, the densities of liquids usually are reported in grams per milliliter (g/mL). The densities of solids often are reported in grams per cubic centimeter (g/cm^3).

VI. Working with Numbers

Measured and Exact Numbers.   Every measurement, no matter how carefully it is made, is subject to some experimental error, since we always estimate the last decimal place. For example, suppose that we use a centimeter ruler, such as that in Figure 1.1, to measure a piece of metal. The smallest divisions of the ruler measure to the nearest tenth of a centimeter. (This corresponds to the nearest millimeter, since 0.1 cm = 1 mm.) Careful inspection reveals that the piece of metal is less than 1.9 cm long, but greater than 1.8 cm. We can estimate its length to be 1.83 cm. It is obvious that this value is more accurate than either 1.8 cm or 1.9 cm. Is it completely accurate? Of course not. Some

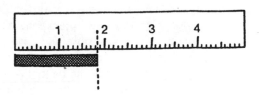

FIGURE 1.1

Use of a centimeter ruler. The length of the object being measured is 1.83 cm.

estimation is necessary, as we might have estimated it to be 1.82 cm or 1.84 cm. Thus, there is an uncertainty about a *measured number* such as this.

On the other hand, if three objects are being counted, the value obtained is exact if we have counted correctly. Three apples means exactly three, no more and no less. This type of number is called an *exact number* to distinguish it from a measured number.

Significant Figures.   When working with measured numbers, we refer to the digits that are actually measured as *significant figures*, or *significant digits*. Thus, there are three significant figures in the 1.83 cm measurement made on the piece of metal mentioned earlier. If we had used a more sophisticated measuring device that provided a value of 1.832 cm, there would be four significant figures.

Whenever calculations are carried out using measured numbers, the calculations cannot be any more accurate than the least accurate measurement in the set of measurements. *When calculations involve multiplication or division, the number of significant figures in the answer must be the same as in the factor with the fewest number of significant figures.* For example, if we wish to convert the 1.83 cm measurement to inches, the answer must be rounded off to three significant figures:

$$? \text{ in.} = 1.83 \text{ cm} \left(\frac{1 \text{ in.}}{2.54 \text{ cm}} \right) = 0.720 \text{ in.}$$

Notice that the zero at the end of the number is significant and must be included since the answer must have three significant figures.

When numbers are added or subtracted, the answer must be rounded off to the same decimal place as is the number entered into the calculation with the fewest digits to the right of the decimal place. For example, suppose two mass measurements were made on different balances, one of which can be read to the nearest 0.01 g and the other to the nearest 0.1 g. The sum of their masses would be rounded off to the nearest 0.1 g:

$$
\begin{array}{r}
43.6 \text{ g} \\
+ \ 132.31 \text{ g} \\
\hline
175.9 \text{ g}
\end{array}
$$

Since 43.6 g has an uncertainty in the tenths column, the sum of the two masses must also have uncertainty in that column, and so the answer may not be reported beyond the tenths place.

Precision and Accuracy.   Since measured quantities contain uncertainty, it is desirable to repeat measurements to be sure that an error has not been made. The degree to which repeated measurements agree with one another is known as the *precision* of the measurement. If the mass of an object is determined three times, and there is good agreement between the three values, the measurement has a high degree of precision. On the other hand, if there is considerable scatter in the data obtained, we would say that the measurement has poor precision.

Accuracy is the degree to which a measured value agrees with the correct value. For example, suppose a balance is not zeroed correctly, or is damaged in some way. Although repeated weighings of the same object might give the same mass (high precision), the value determined probably would have a poor degree of accuracy.

Average Value.   When several measurements are repeated, an average value may be obtained by adding up the values and dividing the sum by the number of values added. For example, suppose the same object is weighed four times, giving the following masses: 43.2 g, 43.3 g, 43.1 g, 43.2 g. The average mass would be calculated as follows:

$$\frac{43.2 \text{ g} + 43.3 \text{ g} + 43.1 \text{ g} + 43.2 \text{ g}}{4} = \frac{172.8 \text{ g}}{4} = 43.2 \text{ g}$$

Percentage Error.   The measurements of many properties of matter are so well established that an accepted value already exists that is considered correct. A newly repeated experimental value may be compared to the correct value by calculating a percentage error. The percentage error is a measure of accuracy. In the experiment, you will be asked to calculate the percentage error between the density you determine for an unknown liquid and its accepted value. A percentage error is calculated by comparing the experimental value to the accepted value as follows:

$$\text{Percentage error} = \frac{|\text{accepted value} - \text{measured value}|}{\text{accepted value}} \times 100\%$$

It makes no real difference whether the measured value is subtracted from the accepted value or whether the accepted value is subtracted from the measured value, since we will take the absolute value (positive sign) of their difference. For example, suppose you determine the density of a liquid to be 1.70 g/mL, and the accepted value is 2.00 g/mL. The percentage error is calculated as follows:

$$\% \text{ error} = \frac{|1.70 \text{ g/mL} - 2.00 \text{ g/mL}|}{2.00 \text{ g/mL}} \times 100\%$$

$$= \frac{0.30 \text{ g/mL}}{2.00 \text{ g/mL}} \times 100\% = 15\%$$

Percentage Difference.   Occasionally we wish to compare two or more values to one another without knowing which of them may be correct. A percentage difference between two (or more) numbers may be obtained by taking the difference between the high and low values, dividing that number by the average value, and then multiplying by 100%:

$$\text{Percentage difference} = \frac{\text{high value} - \text{low value}}{\text{average value}} \times 100\%$$

The percentage difference between the volumes 26.0 mL and 24.0 mL would be calculated as follows:

$$\% \text{ difference} = \frac{26.0 \text{ mL} - 24.0 \text{ mL}}{25.0 \text{ mL}} \times 100\%$$

$$= \frac{2.0 \text{ mL}}{25.0 \text{ mL}} \times 100\% = 8.0\%$$

PRELAB QUESTIONS

1. Convert your height in inches to meters.
2. What Celsius temperature is equivalent to a body temperature of 98.6°F?
3. Suppose you have a box of 10 marbles, a 50 mL graduated cylinder, and some water. How would you measure the volume of a marble? (Assume that all marbles are of equal volume.)
4. Suppose a digital balance reads 0.15 g when there is nothing on the pan. If a beaker is placed on the balance and the balance reads 24.68 g, what is the true mass of the beaker?
5. The density of water at 25°C is 0.997 g/mL. What percentage error would you make if you used the value of 1.000 g/mL at 25°C? (Show your calculations.)

EXPERIMENTAL

Materials
a ruler graduated in centimeters
10 mL graduated cylinder
50 mL graduated cylinder
small test tubes (100 mm tall)
large test tubes (150 mm tall)
50 mL and 150 mL (or 250 mL) beakers
50 mL Erlenmeyer flask
balance
unknown liquids for density determination
irregular solids for density determination
object for classwide length determination

Time Required
3 hours

Cleaning Up
General instructions for disposing of wastes generated in this experiment are provided at the end of each experimental procedure. Additional, more specific information and suggestions for managing hazardous wastes may be found in the *Instructor's Guide*. Your instructor will provide you with special waste handling directions when necessary.

PROCEDURE

I. Length Measurements
Measure the length and width of your laboratory notebook in centimeters. Convert these measurements to inches and to millimeters (1 in. = 2.54 cm).

II. Temperature Measurements
1. The mercury level in a laboratory thermometer rises and falls to read the temperature it is exposed to. It is not necessary to "shake down" a laboratory thermometer. Determine the Celsius temperature in the laboratory by

reading your thermometer. Covert this temperature to Kelvin temperature. Next, convert the Celsius reading to its Fahrenheit equivalent.

2. Prepare an ice water bath by filling halfway either a 150 mL or 250 mL beaker with water and then adding enough ice to bring the volume near the top of the beaker. Immerse your thermometer in the ice bath and stir, taking care not to break the thermometer. Record the temperature. If your reading differs from 0°C by more than two degrees, consult with your instructor.

III.   Volume Measurements

1. The curved surface of a liquid in a cylinder is known as the meniscus. Fill your graduated cylinder about halfway with water, and find the meniscus. Figure 1.2 shows how to read a graduated cylinder. Make a sketch of the meniscus you observe, and indicate where to read the volume on the meniscus.

2. Fill your small test tube with water. Next, pour the water into a 10 mL graduated cylinder. Record the volume by reading the bottom of the meniscus.

3. Fill your large test tube with water. Pour the water into a 50 mL graduated cylinder and record the volume.

4. Fill your 50 mL beaker to the 40 mL mark. Pour the water into a 50 mL graduated cylinder and record the volume. (If your beaker lacks calibration marks, try to estimate where 40 mL would be.)

5. Fill your 50 mL Erlenmeyer flask to the 40 mL mark. Pour the water into a 50 mL graduated cylinder and record the volume. (If your flask lacks calibration marks, try to estimate where 40 mL would be.)

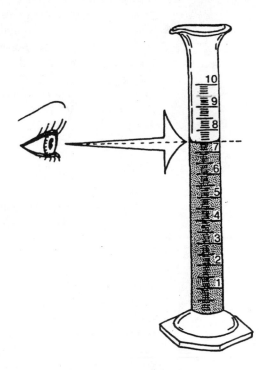

FIGURE 1.2

Reading a graduated cylinder. To obtain the correct reading, your eye must be level with the meniscus, which is read at its lowest point. The meniscus shown reads 7.5 mL.

IV. Mass Measurements

1. Acquaint yourself with the various balances available in your laboratory. The first four figures in the "Laboratory Equipment" section illustrate several balances you are likely to encounter in your work.
2. Weigh a large test tube, a 50 mL beaker, and a 150 mL beaker on a balance selected by your instructor. Your instructor may want you to repeat these measurements on a different balance if more than one type is available. Tabulate the data, including the type(s) of balance(s) used.

V. Density Measurements

1. Weigh a dry 10 mL graduated cylinder. Measure about 2 mL of an unknown liquid (provided by your instructor) into the graduated cylinder. Record the volume of liquid as accurately as the markings on the cylinder permit. Then reweigh the graduated cylinder with the liquid. Calculate the density of the unknown liquid. (Recall that density is mass per unit volume.) Repeat this procedure using about 10 mL of the unknown liquid.

Cleaning Up

Pour your unknown liquid into the bottle(s) supplied by your instructor for this purpose. Your instructor may provide only one bottle, or you may be given special instructions if your instructor wishes to separate unknowns from one another.

2. Report the density determined to your instructor, who will tell you the accepted density of your unknown. Calculate the percentage error for each of your density measurements.
3. The density of an irregular solid can be determined by a method known as water displacement. Meassure the mass of an irregular solid object. Next fill a 50 mL graduated cylinder about halfway with water and record the volume. Slide the irregular object carefully (!) into the graduated cylinder and record the new volume. (Be sure the object is completely immersed in the water. If it is not, remove the object, add some more water, and begin again.) The difference between the two volumes represents the volume of the object. Calculate the density of the solid object.

Cleaning Up

Dry the solid unknown you were given with a paper towel. Return this to your instructor (or your chemistry stockroom) as directed.

VI. Precision and Accuracy (Optional)

1. Your instructor will provide a class object for everyone in the class to measure the length of in centimeters. Record your measurement in your data table and on the blackboard. When everyone has completed this task, record all the values, and calculate the average length determined by the class. Your instructor will provide the class with an "accepted value." Calculate the percentage error between your result and the accepted value. Then calculate the percentage difference between the highest and lowest values reported by the entire class.

EXPERIMENT
4

Properties of Gases

PURPOSE

1. To investigate some physical and chemical properties of a group of gases.
2. To use this information to identify these gases when they are encountered.

DISCUSSION

Several gasses are produced frequently in the laboratory, and it is desirable to be able to identify them by some of their physical and chemical properties. The gases under investigation are hydrogen (H_2), carbon dioxide (CO_2), and oxygen (O_2). You will generate these gases by carrying out the following reactions:

hydrogen: $$Zn + 2\,HCl \rightarrow ZnCl_2 + H_2$$

carbon dioxide: $$CaCO_3 + 2\,HCl \rightarrow CaCl_2 + H_2O + CO_2$$

oxygen: $$H_2O_2 \xrightarrow{MnO_2} 2\,H_2O + O_2$$

You will generate each gas by carrying out the appropriate reaction in a test tube. The gas will then be collected by bubbling it into a bottle or test tube that has been filled with water and inverted in a gas collection trough, such as the one shown on the right in Figure 3.1. Since gas bubbles are less dense than water, they will rise to the surface, thereby displacing the water in the collection vessel.

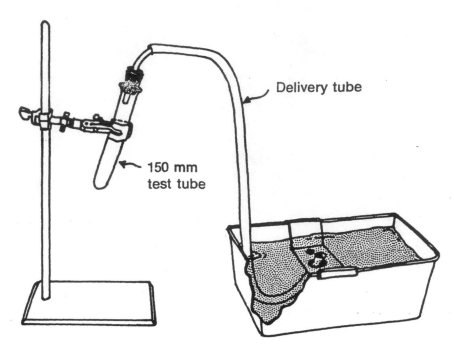

FIGURE 3.1
Gas collection apparatus.

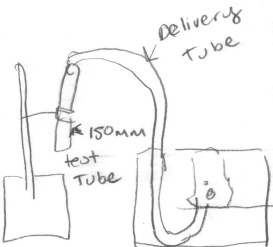

PRELAB QUESTIONS

1. Which of the following mixtures would be most likely to produce carbon dioxide? Explain why you pick the answer you select.
   (a)   magnesium and nitric acid: $Mg + HNO_3$
   (b)   sodium carbonate and sulfuric acid: $Na_2CO_3 + H_2SO_4$ *b/c of The*
   (c)   hydrogen peroxide and copper: $H_2O_2 + Cu$ *presence of C + O*

2. When divers exhale beneath the surface of the water, bubbles rise to the surface. Explain this behavior. *Gases are less dense Then water*

3. Draw a sketch of the setup you will use to collect a test tube full of hydrogen. In your sketch, note where the hydrogen is produced, and trace the path it will take to get from where it is produced to where it will be collected.

EXPERIMENTAL

Materials

pneumatic trough
one-hole rubber stopper with delivery tubing
glass bottles
glass plates
test tubes
test tube clamp
wooden splints
dilute hydrochloric acid (6 *M* HCl)
calcium carbonate
saturated calcium hydroxide (limewater)

mossy zinc
manganese dioxide
10% hydrogen peroxide (H_2O_2)
granulated copper metal

Time Required

3 hours

LABORATORY NOTES

1. If you have not already done so, now would be a good time to read the directions for disposal of laboratory reagents, discussed in the "Laboratory Equipment" section at the beginning of this manual.
2. If you prepare nitrogen dioxide (part IV), wear rubber gloves when handling concentrated nitric acid.

Cleaning Up

General instructions for disposing of wastes generated in this experiment are provided at the end of each experimental procedure. Additional, more specific information and suggestions for managing hazardous wastes may be found in the *Instructor's Guide*. Your instructor will provide you with special waste handling directions when necessary.

PROCEDURE

I. Hydrogen

1. Assemble the gas-generating apparatus shown on the left in Figure 3.1. Use a large test tube to generate the gas. Then set the stopper with the delivery tube on your bench next to the apparatus for when it is needed. Fill the pneumatic trough with water.
2. Fill a second test tube with water. Holding your thumb over the opening, invert the test tube in the pneumatic trough as illustrated in Figure 3.2.
3. Add about 5 mL of water and a small piece of mossy zinc to the large test tube you gathered for the gas generator.
4. Add 5 mL of dilute hydrochloric acid (6 *M* HCl). If the reaction does not produce a steady stream of bubbles, add more acid.
5. Insert the stopper with the delivery tube into the gas-generating test tube. Run the delivery tube into the inverted test tube in the pneumatic trough. Hold it there until the hydrogen gas has replaced the water.
6. Remove the test tube from the water and quickly bring a flaming wooden splint to the mouth of the test tube. (If nothing significant occurs, repeat the procedure.)
7. Record your observations.

Cleaning Up

Dispose of your waste hydrochloric acid with zinc as directed by your instructor.

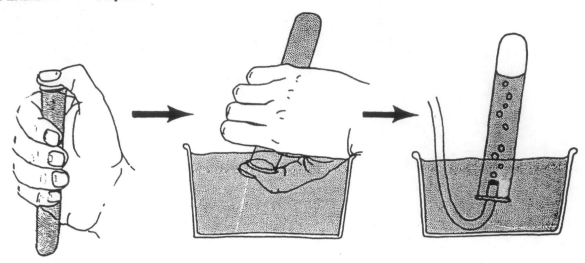

FIGURE 3.2

Preparing a test tube for gas collection. Fill a test tube with water, invert it in the pneumatic trough, and insert the gas delivery tube in the mouth of the test tube. (To prepare a bottle for gas collection, fill it with water, and cover it with a glass plate before inverting.)

II. Carbon Dioxide

1. Prepare your gas-generating apparatus for reuse.
2. Fill three wide-mouth bottles with water. Hold a glass plate over the mouth of each bottle as you invert it in the pneumatic trough.
3. Place several lumps of calcium carbonate in a large test tube and add dilute hydrochloric acid until there is a distinct evolution of carbon dioxide. If the generation of carbon dioxide is inconveniently slow, add small portions of concentrated hydrochloric acid to adjust the rate of evolution.
4. Connect this test tube to the gas-collecting apparatus as you did previously for hydrogen.
5. Fill each bottle with carbon dioxide from the gas generator. Cover the open mouth of each bottle with a glass plate before removing it from the water. Turn each bottle right-side up as it is lifted from the surface of the water, and set the covered bottle on the lab bench until the gas is needed.
6. Note the appearance and odor of the gas.
7. Light a wooden splint and insert it in one of the bottles. Note what happens.
8. Saturated calcium hydroxide solution also is known as limewater. It is used to test for carbon dioxide. Pour about 10 mL of clear limewater into the second bottle, cover with a glass plate, and shake several times. Record your observations.
9. Place about 10 mL of limewater in a fresh bottle containing air only. Take the third bottle of carbon dioxide that you have prepared and hold it over the bottle containing the air and limewater in a tilted position as if you were pouring water. In other words, "pour" the carbon dioxide into the bottle containing limewater. Cover the bottle containing the limewater and shake. Record your observations.

Cleaning Up

Dispose of your waste hydrochloric acid and calcium carbonate as directed by your instructor. Calcium carbonate is not a hazardous substance and may be disposed of in the garbage if rinsed free of acid. Do not allow solid calcium carbonate to go down the drain, as clogging of the plumbing may occur. Used limewater may be disposed of down the drain, followed by rinse water.

III. Oxygen

1. Invert a water-filled bottle in the pneumatic trough.
2. Place about 0.1 g of manganese dioxide in a large test tube. (Enough manganese dioxide to fill the tip of a spatula will be about the right amount.)
3. Add enough 10% hydrogen peroxide to fill the test tube about halfway.
4. Connect the tube to the gas-collecting apparatus, as you did previously.
5. Allow the gas to bubble uncollected for about 1 minute, and then collect the gas (oxygen) in the water-filled bottle.
6. Invert the bottle containing the oxygen. Light a wooden splint and blow out the flame so the splint only glows. Immediately thrust the glowing splint into the bottle containing the oxygen. Record your observations.

EXPERIMENT
5

Liquids and Solids

PURPOSE

1. To determine the boiling point of a liquid.
2. To use the *Handbook of Chemistry and Physics*[*] to obtain the boiling points of other substances.
3. To determine the melting point of a solid.
4. To use the *Handbook of Chemistry and Physics* to obtain the melting points of other substances.
5. To investigate the solvent properties of polar and nonpolar liquids.
6. To investigate the conductivity of aqueous solutions of ionic and covalent substances.

DISCUSSION

In this experiment, you will examine a wide variety of physical properties of liquids and solids. This investigation will introduce you to some concepts that you will encounter throughout the course. Some of the data you will gather would take far too long for you to obtain in the laboratory. Consequently, you will use the *Handbook of Chemistry and Physics* to look up the requested information. We will refer to this useful reference as *the handbook*. Some of the substances you will work with are organic compounds, and others are inorganic compounds. To find the information you need for organic compounds, use the section of the handbook titled "Physical Constants of Organic Compounds." Look up the inorganic compounds in the section called "Physical Constants of Inorganic Compounds." The classification of each compound will be given to you as you proceed with the experiment.

Boiling Point
Two of the more important physical properties of pure substances are the boiling point and melting point. The *boiling point* is the temperature at which a

---

[*] Lide, David R., editor; *Handbook of Chemistry and Physics,* any edition, Cleveland, Ohio, CRC Press.

liquid is converted to its gaseous state. Later, when you study gas laws, you will learn a more formal definition, but this one will suffice for now. Boiling points are sometimes used to determine the purity of substances, since pure substances have distinct boiling points. In this experiment, you will determine the boiling point of one substance experimentally, and look up the boiling points of several others in the handbook. All of the substances whose boiling points you wish to find are organic compounds.

Melting Point

The melting point is an important property of solids. The *melting point* is the temperature at which a solid is converted to liquid. Like the boiling point, the melting point also is used for identification. You will determine the melting point of one substance and look up the melting points of several other substances in the handbook. Some of the solids will be organic compounds, and others will be inorganic substances.

Solubilities

When a solid or liquid dissolves in a liquid, the resulting mixture is called a *solution*. The substance being dissolved is referred to as the *solute*, and the liquid it is dissolved in is the *solvent*. In this experiment, you will study some properties of solvents, solutes, and the solutions that can be prepared from them. Solutions that are prepared with water as the solvent are known as *aqueous* solutions.

Solids and liquids may be classified as polar or nonpolar. A *polar* substance is one in which there is a separation of electrical charge within each molecule. For example, the hydrogen atom in a hydrogen fluoride molecule bears a partial positive charge, whereas the fluorine atom is somewhat negatively charged: $\overset{\delta+}{H} - \overset{\delta-}{F}$. The symbols $\delta+$ and $\delta-$ indicate that these are not full charges, as is the case in ionic substances. You may think of ionic substances as the ultimate polar extreme in which individual molecules no longer exist, but instead the substance is composed of alternating arrays of cations (positive ions) and anions (negative ions). *Nonpolar* substances lack the overall charge separation that characterizes polar substances.

In this portion of the experiment, you will investigate some solvent properties of water (a highly polar liquid), methanol (a liquid with lower polarity than water), ethyl acetate (a nonpolar liquid) and hexane (a nonpolar liquid). You will first determine the mutual solubilities of these liquids with one another. Two liquids that are mutually soluble are said to be *miscible*. However, two liquids that form layers, rather than dissolve, are said to be *immiscible*. You will also determine the solubilities of a variety of solid solutes in each of several solvents. The solids you will test are sodium chloride and potassium nitrate (two ionic solids), sucrose (a polar covalent solid), iodine (a nonpolar solid), and paraffin (also nonpolar). The solvents you will use are water, methanol (methyl alcohol), hexane, and ethyl acetate.

PRELAB QUESTIONS

1. Substance A has a melting point of −10°C and a boiling point of 57°C. Substance B has a melting point of −67°C and a boiling point of 15°C. Room temperature is 20°C.
   (a) What is the physical state (solid, liquid, or gas) of substance A at room temperature? At 0°C? At 100°C?
   (b) What is the physical state (solid, liquid, or gas) of substance B at room temperature? At 0°C? At 100°C?
2. Oil and vinegar are immiscible. When oil and vinegar salad dressing is shaken, the oil always comes to the top upon separating. Why?
3. In part V, several substances will be dissolved and their conductivities measured. Why is it important to first measure the conductivity of water?
4. Naphthalene is a nonpolar solid that is used in mothballs. It is soluble in hexane but not in water. What can you conclude about the polarity of hexane? Explain your answer.

EXPERIMENTAL

Materials

600 mL beaker
glass beads
universal clamp
thermometer
capillary tubing (sealed at one end)
test tubes
beakers

ring stand
2-propanol
acetamide
ethyl acetate
hexane
methanol (methyl alcohol)
iodine crystals
sodium chloride
sucrose
potassium nitrate
paraffin
urea

Time Required
3 to 4 hours

LABORATORY NOTES

1. 2-Propanol is a flammable liquid that can ignite if it is brought too close to an open flame. Nevertheless, the boiling point of 2-propanol may be determined safely using the procedure described. *Do not attempt to heat the test tube directly with a Bunsen burner. That would create a fire hazard.* As an additional safety precaution, keep several wet paper towels next to the ring stand. If the 2-propanol should ignite, simply cover the opening of the test tube with the wet towels to extinguish the flame.

2. Ethyl acetate fumes can become irritating if inhaled over a prolonged period of time. If hood space permits, carry out the solubility tests under the hood. If that is not possible, keep the solvents you use in stoppered test tubes, except when dispensing them for the tests you are carrying out.

3. Your instructor will tell you how to dispose of waste materials from this experiment.

4. Be very careful when using the conductivity apparatus. This apparatus should only be plugged in when the electrodes are actually immersed in a solution being tested. It should be unplugged in between all tests.

Cleaning Up
General instructions for disposing of wastes generated in this experiment are provided at the end of each experimental procedure. Additional, more specific information and suggestions for managing hazardous wastes may be found in the *Instructor's Guide*. Your instructor will provide you with special waste handling directions when necessary.

PROCEDURE

I. **Boiling Points (See Laboratory Note 1.)**

1. Put about 5 mL of 2-propanol in a large test tube. Add two or three small glass beads to serve as boiling chips. Set this in your test tube rack until you are ready for it in the next step.

2. Assemble the apparatus shown in Figure 4.2. Use a 600 mL beaker for the water bath, and fill it about half full with tap water. Clamp the test tube with a universal clamp and attach it to the ringstand so that the bottom of

the test tube is immersed in the water bath. Arrange the height of the test tube so that the surface of the 2-propanol is close to that of the water. Suspend the thermometer so that it is about 5 cm (2 in.) above the surface of the 2-propanol and does not touch the sides of the test tube.

3. Light your Bunsen burner and heat the water bath. Be sure that the flames from your Bunsen burner do not spread out around the sides of the beaker. Watch the thermometer once the 2-propanol begins to boil. Vapors should condense on the thermometer and drop back into the liquid. The temperature should climb and then reach a stable point. This is the boiling point. Record it.

4. Look up the accepted value for the boiling point of 2-propanol in the organic section of the handbook. It is entered under *2-propanol*.

5. Look up the boiling points and molecular masses of the following hydrocarbons in the organic section of the handbook: methane (CH_4), ethane (C_2H_6), propane (C_3H_8), butane (C_4H_{10}), pentane (C_5H_{12}), hexane (C_6H_{14}), heptane (C_7H_{16}), octane (C_8H_{18}), nonane (C_9H_{20}), and decane $(C_{10}H_{22})$. (The handbook may refer to the molecular mass by the older term "molecular weight.")

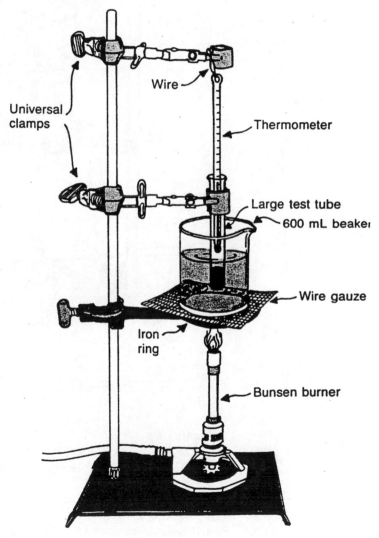

FIGURE 4.2
Apparatus for determining the boiling point of a substance.

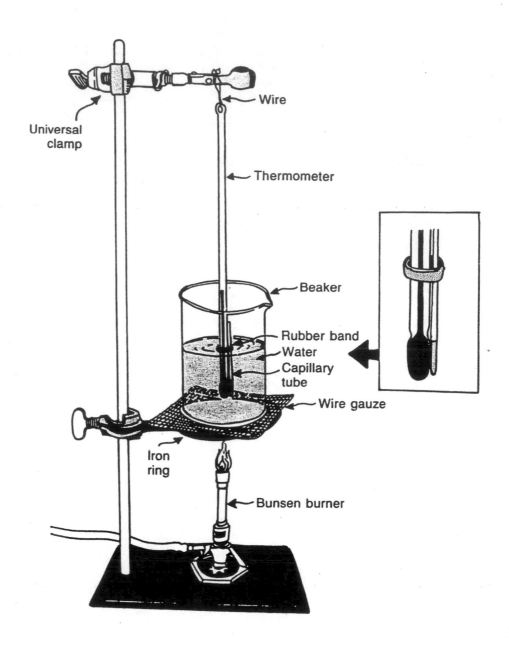

FIGURE 4.3
Apparatus for determining the melting point of a substance.

Cleaning Up

Dispose of your used 2-propanol in the bottle provided for this purpose. This liquid may be reused if not contaminated.

II.   Melting Points

1. Push the open end of a capillary tube into a small quantity of acetamide. Tap the closed end of the tube on the lab bench to pack the crystals to a depth of about 2 mm. Attach the capillary tube to a thermometer with a piece of string or a rubber band.

2. Fill a 250 mL beaker about half full of water. Lower the thermometer into the water so that the lower end of the capillary tube is below the surface (Fig. 4.3).

3. Heat the water slowly (2° to 4° per minute). Note the temperature at which the acetamide melts.

4. Look up the melting point of acetamide in the handbook. (It is an organic substance entered under *acetamide* or *acetic acid, amide.*) Compare your experimental result with the accepted value.

5. Look up the melting points of the following covalent solids in the handbook: naphthalene, iodine, sucrose, and urea. (Naphthlene, sucrose, and urea are organic substances; iodine is an inorganic substance.) Look up the melting points of the following ionic salts: sodium chloride, potassium nitrate, calcium carbonate, and iron(III) chloride. (These are all inorganic substances.)

Cleaning Up

Dispose of your waste capillary tubes in the container provided for this purpose. Dispose of any unused acetamide in the bottle provided for this purpose. Unused acetamide may be reused if not contaminated.

III. Miscibility

To reduce the volume of hazardous waste generated by this experiment, your instructor may choose to set up this section as a demonstration for you to observe. In that event, test tubes 1 through 6 will be set in a test tube holder in a location where you can observe them. Shake each of the six stoppered test tubes as directed in step 3 below. Record your observations.

1. Label six large test tubes 1 – 6.

2. To the first add about 3 mL water and 3 mL ethyl acetate. To the second add 3 mL water and 3 mL methanol. To the third add 3 mL water and 3 mL hexane. To the fourth add 3 mL methanol and 3 mL ethyl acetate. To the fifth add 3 mL methanol and 3 mL hexane. To the sixth add 3 mL ethyl acetate and 3 mL hexane.

3. Stopper and shake the contents of each test tube. Which of these combinations are miscible? Which are immiscible? Record your observations.

Cleaning Up

Dispose of the combined wastes from all six test tubes in the waste container set aside for this purpose. This container may be labeled, "Non-halogenated, flammable waste organic solvents."

IV. Solubility of Solids in Liquids

1. Label four clean test tubes 1 – 4.

2. Put about 3 mL of water in the first test tube, 3 mL of methanol in the second, 3 mL of hexane in the third, and 3 mL of ethyl acetate in the fourth.

3. Add one crystal of iodine to each of the test tubes, shake, and observe.

4. Repeat the procedure using one crystal (or an equivalent amount) of each of the following solids instead of iodine: sodium chloride, sucrose, potassium nitrate, and paraffin.

5. Make a table in your notebook for your observations.   Note which substances are soluble and which are insoluble.

Cleaning Up

You may dispose of the aqueous solutions (those with water) of sodium chloride, sucrose, and potassium nitrate down the drain.   Dispose of all other wastes as directed by your instructor.

Physical and Chemical Properties of Substances

1. To investigate the chemical and physical properties of pure chemical substances.
2. To use the *Handbook of Chemistry and Physics* to find information about the physical properties of pure substances.
3. To use the information obtained about specific compounds and elements to separate the components of a mixture.

DISCUSSION

Pure substances may be described by their physical and chemical properties. A property of a substance is some distinguishing characteristic. Among the physical properties commonly used to characterize pure substances are taste, color, odor, hardness, solubility in various solvents, density, melting point, and boiling point. The observation of these physical properties does not involve any chemical change in the substance. For example, lead is a solid at ordinary temperatures, has a characteristic color, and has a density of 11.34 g/cm^3 at 16°C. When lead is heated to 327.4°C, it melts. However, allowing the molten sample to cool below this temperature will return it to its original solid state. Since no chemical change has taken place, the melting point of lead is considered to be one of its physical properties. Similarly, observing its color or measuring its density does not involve any chemical change. Thus, color and density are also physical properties.

Chemical properties describe the tendencies of a substance to undergo chemical change. For example, when copper is heated in a flame, the surface of the metal turns black. Cooling will not restore the copper to its original color. At high temperatures copper reacts with oxygen to produce a new compound, copper(II) oxide. A chemical reaction takes place on the surface of the metal. Each new product formed as a result of a chemical change has its own set of characteristic chemical and physical properties.

Chemical and physical properties help the chemist to identify substances. For example, copper and gold are two metals with similar colors. When copper is treated with nitric acid, however, it undergoes a reaction and goes into solution. A characteristic blue color is imparted to the solution as the copper dissolves in the nitric acid. In contrast to this, gold neither reacts nor dissolves in nitric acid. The difference in the reactivities of these two metals with nitric acid would assist us in their identification. Similarly, determining the densities of these metals would be useful for identifying each.

In this experiment, you will examine several physical and chemical properties of a number of elements and compounds. The elements to be tested are magnesium, copper, and zinc. The compounds to be tested are magnesium oxide, copper(II) carbonate, copper(II) nitrate, and sodium chloride. You should record your observations in a data table, such as the one provided at the end of this experiment.

In this experiment, you will be asked to filter a solution that has an insoluble residue suspended in it. The liquid solution in this type of mixture is known as a *filtrate*. Upon filtering this mixture, the residue will remain in the filter, while the filtrate passes through the funnel and is collected below.

PRELAB QUESTIONS

1. A substance dissolves in acid producing a gas. Is this a physical change or a chemical change? Explain.
2. If you place a large quantity of sucrose (table sugar) in a test tube and add a few drops of water, the sucrose will not dissolve. Does this prove that sucrose is insoluble in water? Explain. How would you determine whether or not sucrose is soluble in water?
3. Substance A dissolves in water but is insoluble in hydrochloric acid. Substance B dissolves in hydrochloric acid because of a chemical reaction, but it is insoluble in water. What would be the best way to separate substance A from substance B if you had a mixture of the two?

EXPERIMENTAL

Materials

dilute sodium hydroxide, 6 M NaOH
dilute hydrochloric acid, 6 M HCl
concentrated hydrochloric acid, 12 M HCl
magnesium, Mg
copper metal, Cu
granular zinc, Zn
magnesium oxide, MgO
copper(II) carbonate, $CuCO_3$
copper(II) nitrate, $Cu(NO_3)_2$
sodium chloride, NaCl
a mixture of copper(II) carbonate and sodium chloride
150 mL beaker
250 mL beaker
test tubes
funnel and filter paper
wash bottle

Time Required
3 hours

LABORATORY NOTES

1. The test tube in which magnesium is heated may become damaged.
2. Before carrying out the separation of the mixture, you will need to read the discussion of gravity filtration in the "Laboratory Equipment" section o this manual.
3. If a drying oven is used in part II, be sure the temperature stays at 100°C o below to avoid charring the filter paper.

Cleaning Up

General instructions for disposing of wastes generated in this experiment are provided at the end of each experimental procedure. Additional, more spe cific information and suggestions for managing hazardous wastes may be found in the *Instructor's Guide*.   Your instructor will provide you with special waste handling directions when necessary.

PROCEDURE

I.   **Observation of Chemical and Physical Properties**
1. Put about 5 mL of dilute hydrochloric acid (6 *M* HCl) in one test tube and 5 mL of dilute sodium hydroxide (6 *M* NaOH) in another. Use this suppl at your laboratory station. You will use these reagents to test the following elements and compounds: magnesium, copper, zinc, magnesium oxide copper(II) carbonate, copper(II) nitrate, and sodium chloride.
2. Carry out the following steps on each of the substances to be tested. Com plete all of the tests on each substance before proceeding to the next Record your data in a table such as that provided in the report sheet fo this experiment.
    (a) Place several crystals (about 0.1 g) of the substance to be tested in eacl of four small test tubes. Examine and record the color.
    test tube 1:
    (b) Heat the sample in the first tube and observe the effect of heat on the substance. Note the evolution of any gases.
    test tube 2:
    (c) Add about 2 mL of water from your wash bottle to the sample in the second test tube. Stir. Observe the solubility of the substance in cold water.
    (d) Gently heat the water just to boiling to observe the solubility of the substance in hot water.
    (e) Allow the solution to cool and test it with litmus paper.
    test tube 3:
    (f) Add a few drops of dilute hydrochloric acid to the sample in the third test tube. Stir. Record any apparent reaction or solubility.
    test tube 4:
    (g) Add a few drops of dilute sodium hydroxide to the sample in the fourth test tube. Stir. Record any apparent reaction or solubility.

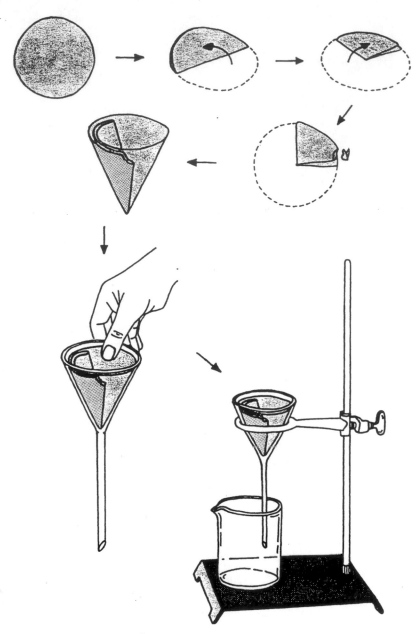

FIGURE 6.1
Preparing a filter paper and funnel for gravity filtration.

3. Check as many of your observations as possible by looking up the substances tested in the *Handbook of Chemistry and Physics*. Use the section titled "Physical Constants of Inorganic Compounds." If your observations do not agree with the information in the handbook, make a note of the disagreement and recheck your observations.

Cleaning Up

Dispose of all waste solids and solutions as directed by your instructor.

EXPERIMENT
7

Specific Heat of a Metal

PURPOSE

1. To measure the specific heat of a metal.
2. To use the results to estimate the atomic weight.

DISCUSSION

Energy can exist in many different forms. The form of energy often encountere when examining physical and chemical changes is *heat energy*. *Heat* is a form energy that flows from an object at a higher temperature to one at a low temperature. The most commonly used measurement for heat energy is the jou (J). A joule is an energy unit obtained:

$$1\,\text{joule} = \frac{1\,\text{kg}\cdot\text{m}^2}{\text{sec}^2}$$

When two objects having different heat energy come in contact with one anothe the two objects will reach a state of thermal equilibrium, where they are at tl same final temperature. The heat lost by the hotter object will equal the he gained by the cooler one.

The heat involved in a temperature change depends on three factors: the ma (m) of the object, the temperature change (Δt) of the object and the specific he (c) of the substance. *Specific heat* is defined as the heat needed to raise tl temperature one gram of the substance by one-Celsius degree. Its units a expressed as J/g-C°. Water has a specific heat of 4.184 J/g-C°.

Heat, Q, (in Joules) is calculated by the equation:

$$Q = mc\Delta t$$

In this experiment the metal's specific heat is not known. Therefore, we cannot calculate Q for the metal, but we can calculate the Q gained by the water. Assuming no heat loss to or gain by the surroundings:

$$\textbf{Q (gained by the water)} = \textbf{Q (lost by the metal)}$$

or

$$Q_m = m_m c_m \Delta t_m \quad \text{and} \quad Q_w = m_w c_w \Delta t_w$$

where the subscripts refer to the metal, m and water, w.

EXPERIMENTAL

Materials
400-mL beaker
calorimeter
ring stand
test tube clamp
thermometer
unknown metal sample

Time Required
2 ½ hours

Cleaning Up
Dry the unknown metal sample on paper towels. Place the unknown metal in the large test tube and return to the laboratory cart.

$$Q = (21.469 g)(4.184 \, J/g°)(3.3°C)$$
$$296.4$$

PROCEDURE

Determine the mass of the unknown metal by taring a large empty test tube (standing in a beaker) to zero and adding the metal sample to the clean dry test tube. Assemble the hot water bath as shown. Fill a 400-mL beaker about two-thirds with water and heat it to boiling. Place the test tube containing the metal in a test tube clamp. Attach the test tube clamp to the ring stand so that the test tube is suspended in the hot water. Be sure that the water level in the beaker is above the metal level in the test tube, and that the test tube does not rest on the bottom of the beaker. Continue to heat the water after it has begun boiling to ensure that the metal is at the same temperature as the boiling water. Measure the water temperature with a thermometer.

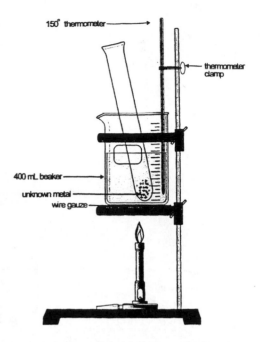

Assemble the calorimeter as shown. The calorimeter consists of two nesting styrofoam cups with a cover and a hole for a thermometer. Weigh the styrofoam cups, add about 50 mL of water to it and weigh again. Measure the temperature of the water to the nearest 0.1°C. After the metal has been in the boiling water for at least ten minutes, quickly, and in one motion, remove it from the water and pour the metal into the styrofoam calorimeter. (Avoid allowing any hot water to fall in the cup.) Replace the cover on the calorimeter, and use the thermometer to stir the metal and water. Record to 0.1°C the highest temperature reached by the water.

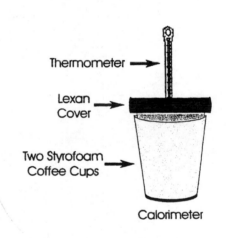

Dry the metal sample by heating it in the hot water bath in a test tube and then spreading it out on a dry paper towel. Repeat the experiment using a dry test tube and a fresh sample of water. Use approximately 40-mL of water for the second trial. When the experiment has been completed, dry the sample again and return it to the test tube from which it originally came.

empty test tube:
30.921 g

test tube +
metal: 52.390 g

mass of unknown:
21.469 g

~~284.454~~
~~192.969~~ g Beaker + test tube
~~600 mL~~

192.967 g 400 mL

Determining the Empirical Formula of Magnesium Oxide

prepared by **M. L. Gillette**, Indiana University Kokomo;
H. A. Neidig, Lebanon Valley College; and **J. N. Spencer**, Franklin and Marshall College

Purpose of the Experiment

Determine the empirical formula of magnesium oxide.

Background Required

You should be familiar with basic laboratory techniques for measuring mass and using a Bunsen burner, and the concepts associated with chemical formulas, molar mass, and ionic compounds.

Background Information

To understand the behavior of a chemical compound we must first know its chemical formula. The simplest molar combining ratio of the elements in a compound is called the **empirical formula.** We can determine the ratio if we know the mass of the individual elements in a known mass of the compound. For most ionic compounds, compounds formed from metals and nonmetals, the empirical formula is the same as the compound formula. For covalent compounds, compounds formed from nonmetals, the empirical formula is not necessarily the same as the molecular formula of the compound. For example, the empirical formula of water, H_2O, is the same as its molecular formula. In contrast, the empirical formula of hydrogen peroxide is HO, but its molecular formula is H_2O_2. To determine whether or not a covalent compound's empirical and molecular formulas are the same, we need to know the molar mass of the compound.

We can form an oxide of a metal by heating the metal in air. If we know the mass of metal heated and the mass of metal oxide formed, we can determine the empirical formula of the metal oxide produced.

Example

Problem Determine the empirical formula of an oxide of titanium (Ti). A 3.45-g Ti sample is heated in an open vessel to produce a compound containing Ti and oxygen (O), Ti_xO_y. The mass of the product is 5.76 g.

Solution *(1) Calculate the mass of O that combined with the Ti.*

$$\text{mass of O, g} = \text{mass of oxide, g} - \text{mass of metal, g}$$
$$= 5.76 \text{ g} - 3.45 \text{ g} = 2.31 \text{ g O}$$

(2) Calculate the number of moles of Ti that reacted. The molar mass of Ti is 47.9 g/mol.

$$\text{number of moles of Ti, mol} = (\text{mass of Ti, g})\left(\frac{1 \text{ mol Ti}}{47.9 \text{ g Ti}}\right) = (3.45 \text{ g Ti})\left(\frac{1 \text{ mol Ti}}{47.9 \text{ g Ti}}\right) = 7.20 \times 10^{-2} \text{ mol Ti}$$

(3) Calculate the number of moles of O that combined with 7.20×10^{-2} mol of Ti. The molar mass of O is 16.0 g/mol.

$$\text{number of moles of O, mol} = (\text{mass of O, g})\left(\frac{1 \text{ mol O}}{16.0 \text{ g O}}\right) = (2.31 \text{ g O})\left(\frac{1 \text{ mol O}}{16.0 \text{ g O}}\right) = 0.144 \text{ mol O}$$

(4) FInd the simplest ratio of the number of moles of Ti to the number of moles of O. Divide the number of moles of Ti and of O by the smaller of the two molar amounts, in this case, the number of moles of Ti.

$$\frac{7.20 \times 10^{-2} \text{ mol Ti}}{7.20 \times 10^{-2}} = 1 \text{ mol Ti}$$

$$\frac{0.144 \text{ mol O}}{7.20 \times 10^{-2}} = 2 \text{ mol O}$$

(5) Write the empirical formula for titanium oxide.
Ti_1O_2, or TiO_2

In This Experiment

You will heat a measured mass of magnesium (Mg) in an open crucible to form a compound containing Mg and O. You will use the masses of the Mg and of the product to calculate the mass of O in the product. Finally, you will determine the empirical formula of the product, magnesium oxide.

Procedure

> **Caution:** *Wear departmentally approved safety goggles while doing this experiment. Always use caution in the laboratory. Many chemicals are potentially harmful. Prevent contact with your eyes, skin, and clothing. Avoid ingesting any of the reagents. Use care when handling objects that become hot during laboratory procedures.*

> **Note:** • *Record sample masses to the nearest milligram (0.001 g) or to the nearest centigram (0.01 g), according to your laboratory instructor's directions.*
> • *Record all of your data on your Data and Observations sheet.*

I. Preparing and Weighing the Crucible and Cover

1. Attach an iron ring to a support stand. Allow sufficient height to place a Bunsen burner beneath the ring, as shown in Figure 1 on the next page.

   Place ceramic-centered wire gauze on the bench beside the support stand.

Note: *Throughout the procedure, use crucible tongs to handle the crucible and its cover. This technique will help to protect your hands from burns. Also, oils and other contaminants will be prevented from being transferred to the crucible.*

2. Place a clay or Nichrome triangle on the ring. Place a clean, dry porcelain crucible at a slight angle on the triangle, as shown in Figure 1. Balance a crucible cover on the open crucible, as shown in Figure 2.

3. Light the Bunsen burner and adjust the gas/air mixture to give a nonluminous flame.

4. Gently heat the crucible for 5 min.

5. Turn off the burner. Place the hot crucible cover on the wire gauze to cool. Then, move the hot crucible from the triangle to the wire gauze to cool.

Note: *An object must be at room temperature for its mass to be accurately determined on a balance.*

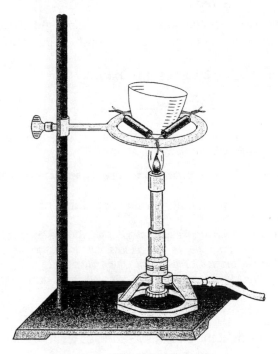

Figure 1 *Apparatus for determination of empirical formula*

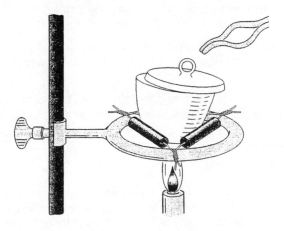

Figure 2 *Position of crucible cover for heating*

6. When you feel no heat as you hold your hand 1–2 cm from the crucible, transfer the crucible and cover to your balance. Determine and record the mass of the crucible and cover.

II. Preparing the Magnesium for Reaction

> **Note:** *If your magnesium appears to have a white oxide coating on it, clean it with sandpaper before proceeding with Step 7.*

7. Obtain an untarnished piece of magnesium ribbon weighing 0.3–0.5 g from your laboratory instructor. Loosely roll the magnesium ribbon into a ball and place it in the crucible.

8. Place the crucible, Mg, and cover on the balance and determine their combined mass. Record this mass.

9. Place the crucible and its contents at a slight angle on the triangle, as shown in Figure 1. Place the crucible cover on the open crucible as shown in Figure 2.

III. Producing Magnesium Oxide

> **Caution:** *The light from the white flame of the burning magnesium can damage your eyes. Never look directly into this flame.*

10. Light the Bunsen burner and adjust it to obtain a nonluminous flame.

> **Note:** *White smoke will appear while you are heating the crucible. This smoke is magnesium oxide. To prevent loss of your product, you should **completely** cover the crucible as soon as you see the white smoke.*
>
> *The Mg has reacted completely when there are no signs of smoke and the contents of the crucible no longer glow brightly.*

11. Gently heat the crucible. As soon as white smoke appears, close the crucible with the cover. Remove the flame.

After 10–15 s, slightly lift the cover and look for white smoke. If smoke is evident, proceed to Step 12. If there is no smoke, proceed to Step 13.

12. Repeat the processes of uncovering, heating, and covering the crucible (repeating Step 11) until you no longer observe white smoke.

13. Position the crucible cover as shown in Figure 2. Position the Bunsen burner so that the flame contacts the bottom of the crucible (see Figure 2). Apply strong heat until the crucible bottom is slightly red. Continue to strongly heat the crucible for 10 min. The crucible should be slightly red throughout the 10-min period.

Turn off the Bunsen burner flame.

> **Note:** *Magnesium also reacts with atmospheric nitrogen (N_2) to form magnesium nitride (Mg_3N_2). Mg_3N_2 is converted to magnesium oxide when it reacts with water. Be careful in Step 14 not to lose any of the white, fluffy solid in the crucible.*
>
> *Before adding water in Step 14, allow the crucible to cool to room temperature. If the crucible is not cool, it may crack when water is added and you will have to begin the procedure again.*

Handle the crucible cover carefully. To cool it, invert the cover on the wire gauze during cooling in Steps 14 and 16. A small amount of product will probably have collected on the cover.

14. Remove the crucible cover, invert it, and place it on the wire gauze to cool. Allow the crucible to remain on the triangle to cool. When the crucible reaches room temperature, use a medicine dropper or Beral pipet to add 10 drops of distilled or deionized water to the crucible.

Replace the cover on the crucible, leaving it slightly ajar, as shown in Figure 2.

Note: *In Step 15, you will heat the crucible to evaporate the excess water. Do not overheat the crucible. Excessive heating will cause spattering, resulting in loss of magnesium oxide from the crucible.*

15. Light the Bunsen burner and adjust it to obtain a nonluminous flame. Gently heat the crucible for 5 min. Then heat the crucible strongly to red heat for 5 min. Turn off the Bunsen burner.

16. Remove the cover, invert it, and place it on the wire gauze to cool. Then remove the crucible from the triangle and place it on the wire gauze to cool.

17. When the crucible is cool, transfer the crucible and the cover to the balance. Weigh the crucible, its contents, and the cover. Record this mass.

18. Discard the magnesium oxide into the Discarded Magnesium Oxide container.

Thoroughly wash the crucible and its cover with tap water. Rinse them with distilled water. Dry them with a disposable towel.

Note: *If your laboratory instructor indicates that there is sufficient time to repeat the experiment, use a clean, dry crucible for the second determination.*

19. If time permits, do a second determination.

Caution: *Wash your hands thoroughly with soap or detergent before leaving the laboratory.*

Irene Herrera

name   partner   section   date

Post-Laboratory Questions

Use the spaces provided for the answers and additional paper if necessary.

1. If you performed two determinations, compare the results of these experiments.

    (a) Would you expect the empirical formula you determined for magnesium oxide to be the same as the one determined by another student?

    Yes The empirical formula would be The same.

    (b) Would you expect an empirical formula to be the same even though different masses of Mg were used? Briefly explain.

    Even Though different masses would be used the ratio within the empirical formula would remain the same

    (c) If different masses of Mg are used, account for any difference in the empirical formulas.

2. A student performed this experiment using magnesium that had a dull, white coating.

    (a) What was the probable identity of the dull coating?

    (b) What effect would the presence of this coating have on the experimentally determined mass of magnesium in magnesium oxide? Briefly explain.

3. When a student removed the crucible cover after the first strong heating (Step 13), some of the white solid was knocked from the cover to the floor and lost. Did this loss cause the calculated number of moles of oxygen in the compound to be too high or too low? Briefly explain.

4. A student wanting to leave the laboratory early weighed the cooled crucible from Step 13 and used this mass as the mass of the crucible, cover, and magnesium oxide. Would this produce a calculated number of moles of oxygen in magnesium oxide that is too high or too low? Briefly explain.

5. A student found that 1.19 g of chromium (Cr) formed 1.74 g of chromium oxide. The molar mass of Cr is 52.00 g/mol. What is the empirical formula of chromium oxide?

_I_

name   partner   section   date

Data and Observations

	determination	
	1	**2**
mass of crucible and cover, g	31.467g	31.467g
mass of crucible, cover, and Mg, g	31.787 g	31.787 g
mass of crucible, cover, and magnesium oxide, g	31.967g	31.961

Calculations and Conclusions

Show your calculations in the spaces provided. Remember to include units with all calculated results.

III. Producing Magnesium Oxide

1. Calculate the mass of Mg reacted.

   determination 1 ___0.32 g___   determination 2 ___0.32 g___

2. Calculate the mass of magnesium oxide formed.

   determination 1 ___0.5 g___   determination 2 ___0.5 g___

3. Calculate the mass of O that combined with the Mg.

   determination 1 ___0.18 g___   determination 2 ___0.18 g___

4. Calculate the average number of moles of Mg that reacted. The molar mass of Mg is 24.31 g/mol.

$$24.31 \rightarrow \frac{1 \text{ mole Mg}}{24.31 \text{g Mg}} = .3200 \text{g} \left(\frac{1 \text{ mole Mg}}{24.31 \text{g}} \right)$$

$$1.31 \times 10^{-2}$$

   average number of moles of Mg ___1.31×10^{-2}___

5. Calculate the average number of moles of O that combined with the Mg. The molar mass of O is 16.00 g/mol.

average number of moles of O _____

6. Find the simplest ratio of the average number of moles of Mg to the average number of moles of O.

(a) Divide the average number of moles of Mg by the smaller of the average numbers of moles of Mg or of O.

(b) Divide the average number of moles of O by the smaller of the average numbers of moles of Mg or of O.

7. Write the empirical formula for the oxide of magnesium.

Pre-Laboratory Assignment

1.   Why is it hazardous for you to look directly at the Mg in the crucible when it is heated and first reacts with atmospheric oxygen?

2.   (a) Why should you always use crucible tongs when you handle the crucible and its cover?

(b) Why will you have to begin the Procedure again if the crucible cover falls and breaks at any time after you complete Step 6?

(c) Why will you add a few drops of water to the white reaction product in the crucible (Step 14)?

(d) Why will the crucible and its contents gain mass as a result of heating the Mg in air?

3. A student determined the empirical formula of potassium oxide using the procedure of this experiment. She obtained the following data:

mass of crucible and cover, g	28.288
mass of crucible, cover, and K, g	28.709
mass of crucible, cover, and potassium oxide, g	28.793

Use these data to determine the empirical formula of potassium oxide. The molar mass of potassium (K) is 39.10 g/mol.

EXPERIMENT 9 ANAL 605

modular · laboratory · program · in · chemistry

publisher: H. A. Neidig   editor: M. L. Gillette

Determining the Percent Water in an Unknown Hydrate

prepared by **M. L. Gillette**, Indiana University Kokomo; **H. A. Neidig**, Lebanon Valley College; and **J. N. Spencer**, Franklin and Marshall College

Purpose of the Experiment

Determine the percent water in an unknown hydrate.

Background Required

You should be familiar with basic laboratory techniques for measuring mass and using a Bunsen burner. You should understand the concepts associated with stoichiometry.

Background Information

Many solid ionic compounds contain weakly bound water molecules within their crystal structures. We call such solids **hydrates** and the bound water molecules we call **water(s) of hydration.** We include the water(s) of hydration in the name and chemical formula for a hydrate, connecting the water(s) to the rest of the formula with a raised dot. For example, the chemical formula for copper(II) sulfate pentahydrate is $CuSO_4 \cdot 5H_2O$.

We can remove the water(s) of hydration from a hydrate using a process called **dehydration**, leaving the **anhydrous** ("without water") form of the compound. We usually dehydrate compounds by heating them. For example, when we heat blue $CuSO_4 \cdot 5H_2O$, the waters of hydration are released as water vapor, and solid, white anhydrous $CuSO_4$ remains, as shown in Equation 1.

$$CuSO_4 \cdot 5H_2O(s, \text{blue}) \xrightarrow{\text{heat}} CuSO_4(s, \text{white}) + 5\,H_2O(g) \quad \text{(Eq. 1)}$$

Example

Problem   The mass of a clean, dry crucible is 10.427 g. The mass of the crucible after the addition of a sample of unknown green hydrate is 12.179 g. After heating, the crucible plus solid yellow residue weighs 11.459 g. Determine the percent water in the unknown hydrate.

Solution   (a) *Calculate the mass of hydrate heated.*
$$12.179 \text{ g} - 10.427 \text{ g} = 1.752 \text{ g}$$

(b) *Calculate the mass of water in the hydrate sample.*
$$12.179 \text{ g} - 11.459 \text{ g} = 0.720 \text{ g}$$

(c) *Calculate the percent water in the hydrate sample, using Equation 2.*

$$\text{percent water, \%} = \left(\frac{\text{mass of water lost, g}}{\text{mass of hydate heated, g}} \right)(100\%) = \left(\frac{0.720 \text{ g}}{1.752 \text{ g}} \right)(100\%) = 41.1\% \quad \text{(Eq. 2)}$$

In This Experiment

You will determine the mass of a hydrated salt sample and the mass of the residue after heating the sample. From these masses, you will calculate the mass of water lost during heating and the percent water in the hydrate.

Procedure

> **Caution:** *Wear departmentally approved safety goggles while doing this experiment. Always use caution in the laboratory. Many chemicals are potentially harmful. Prevent contact with your eyes, skin, and clothing. Avoid ingesting any of the reagents. Use care when handling hot objects.*

Note:
- *Clean your crucible according to your laboratory instructor's directions.*
- *Always use crucible tongs to handle the crucible and its cover, in order to avoid contaminating the crucible and cover with finger oils and to prevent burns from the hot crucible.*
- *If you need assistance, either in adjusting your Bunsen burner to obtain a nonluminous flame, or in heating your sample both gently and strongly, consult your laboratory instructor.*
- *Record all masses to either the nearest milligram (0.001 g) or nearest centigram (0.01 g), as indicated by your laboratory instructor.*
- *Record all data on your Data and Observations sheet.*
- *If you perform a second determination, obtain a second clean, dry crucible and cover for that determination.*
- *Dispose of your reaction mixtures according to your laboratory instructor's directions.*

I. Preparing and Weighing the Crucible

1. Obtain an unknown hydrate sample from your laboratory instructor. Record the identification code of your hydrate.

2. Attach a support ring to a ring stand. Place a pipe-stem triangle on the ring. Using crucible tongs, place a clean, dry porcelain crucible on the triangle.

   Place a ceramic-centered wire gauze on the laboratory bench, beside the support stand.

3. Gently heat the crucible for 5 min, using a nonluminous Bunsen burner flame.

   Extinguish the burner flame. Using the tongs, move the hot crucible from th triangle to the wire gauze to cool.

   > **Note:** *In order to accurately determine the mass of an object, be sure that the object is at room temperature.*

II. Heating and Weighing the Unknown Hydrate

4. When you feel no heat when holding your hand 1–2 cm from the crucible, weigh it. Record this mass. Leave the crucible on the balance pan.

Pre-Laboratory Assignment

1. (a) State two reasons why you should always use crucible tongs to handle the crucible in this experiment.

Gram scales are sensitive enough to where oils from skin may effect the wieght of a sample.

(b) How will you determine that your crucible has returned to room temperature after heating?

By placeholding a hand 1-2 cm from the crucible and not feeling heat.

(c) Why is it important to allow your crucible to cool to room temperature before weighing it?

2. (a) What do we mean by the phrase "water(s) of hydration"?

Bound water Molecules

(b) Briefly describe the difference between a hydrate and its anhydrous form.

3. A student followed the Procedure of this experiment, using her unknown hydrate, and obtained the following data.

mass of crucible, g	10.439
mass of crucible and hydrate, g	11.844
mass of crucible and dehydrated sample, g	11.213

(a) Calculate the mass of hydrate heated.

(b) Calculate the mass of water in the hydrate.

(c) Calculate the percent water in the hydrate.

EXPERIMENT 10

Stoichiometry: Preparation of an Insoluble Ionic Compound

PURPOSE

1. To plan and carry out the synthesis of a given amount of an insol[uble] compound.

DISCUSSION

Ionic compounds may be prepared through various types of reactions. In [this] experiment, you will plan the preparation of an assigned compound using on[e of] the methods discussed here. Your instructor will assign you a substanc[e to] prepare. Using the information provided in this discussion, you will devi[se a] synthesis from the available list of reagents given in the experimental sect[ion.] To accomplish this you must first write a reaction that will produce the ass[ign-] ed compound, and then calculate the masses of reactant to be used. The dis[cus-] sion that follows will provide you with the background you need to carry [out] the assignment.

METHODS OF SALT PREPARATION

Neutralization of an Acid with a Base

When an acid and base neutralize one another, the products are a salt [and] water. The salt is an ionic compound that results from a combination of [the] cation of the base and the anion of the acid. For example, when sulfuric aci[d is] completely neutralized with sodium hydroxide, the salt that results is sod[ium] sulfate:

$$H_2SO_4(aq) + 2\,NaOH(aq) \rightarrow Na_2SO_4(aq) + 2\,H_2O(l)$$

If the quantities of materials are carefully selected so that the number of moles of sodium hydroxide is exactly twice the number of moles of sulfuric acid, the aqueous solution containing the product will be composed exclusively of sodium sulfate and water. Evaporation of the water would leave a residue of sodium sulfate.

Reaction of a Metal with an Acid

Many metallic salts can be prepared by reaction of the elemental metal with an acid containing the desired anion. For example, zinc chloride is readily prepared by the reaction of zinc metal with hydrochloric acid:

$$Zn(s) + 2\,HCl(aq) \rightarrow ZnCl_2(aq) + H_2(g)$$

The gaseous hydrogen produced would bubble out of the reaction mixture, leaving behind an aqueous solution of the desired salt. As in the neutralization example, the product could be isolated by evaporating the water present.

Reactions of a Carbonate with an Acid

Certain metallic and nonmetallic salts are most readily prepared by the reaction of a carbonate containing the desired cation with an acid containing the desired anion. For example, ammonium nitrate may be prepared by the reaction of ammonium carbonate with nitric acid:

$$(NH_4)_2CO_3(aq) + 2\,HNO_3(aq) \rightarrow 2\,NH_4NO_3(aq) + H_2O(l) + CO_2(g)$$

The gaseous carbon dioxide produced would bubble out of the reaction mixture, and the water produced would simply add to the water already present, resulting in an aqueous solution of the desired salt. The product could be isolated as described previously.

This method is particularly useful for preparing salts of certain metals that react violently with acids. For example, the reaction of sodium metal with hydrochloric acid might look like a reasonable way to make sodium chloride. However, that reaction is dangerously violent due to the extreme reactivity of sodium. The reaction of sodium carbonate with hydrochloric acid, on the other hand, proceeds smoothly with little or no hazard:

$$Na_2CO_3(aq) + 2\,HCl(aq) \rightarrow 2\,NaCl(aq) + H_2O(l) + CO_2(g)$$

Precipitation

Many ionic substances are relatively insoluble in water. When a solution containing the cation of such a substance is mixed with a solution containing the anion, the substance will precipitate. For example, lead(II) iodide, PbI_2, is an insoluble ionic compound that may be prepared in this fashion. To prepare lead(II) iodide, we would mix a solution containing lead(II) ions with one containing iodide ions. Since we would need solutions of each, we might choose to react lead(II) nitrate (a soluble lead(II) salt) with sodium iodide (a soluble iodide). It is helpful to remember that all nitrate salts are soluble, as are all common alkali metal salts.

The compound that you will be assigned should be prepared by precipitation. You will calculate the masses of each reactant you propose to use, dissolve each separately in water, mix the solutions, and filter the precipitate. After drying the precipitate, you will weigh your product and calculate the percentage yield.

For example, suppose you are assigned the preparation of 6.00 g of lead(II) iodide, and you desire to use the reaction just described:

$$Pb(NO_3)_2(aq) + 2\ NaI(aq) \rightarrow PbI_2(s) + 2\ NaNO_3(aq)$$

The reaction of these two solutions would result in the precipitation of lead(II) iodide, and sodium nitrate would remain behind in solution. To devise an actual procedure for doing this, it is necessary to perform a stoichiometric calculation and determine the masses of lead(II) nitrate and sodium iodide that must react together to produce 6.00 g PbI_2.

Let us begin by calculating the moles of lead(II) iodide we wish to produce:

$$?\ mol\ PbI_2 = 6.00\ g\ PbI_2 \left(\frac{1\ mol\ PbI_2}{461.0\ g\ PbI_2} \right) = 0.0130\ mol\ PbI_2$$

Next, we will calculate the masses of lead(II) nitrate and of sodium iodide required to produce the desired amount of lead(II) iodide:

$$?\ g\ Pb(NO_3)_2 = 0.0130\ mol\ PbI_2 \left(\frac{1\ mol\ Pb(NO_3)_2}{1\ mol\ PbI_2} \right) \left(\frac{331.2\ g\ Pb(NO_3)_2}{1\ mol\ Pb(NO_3)_2} \right)$$

$$= 4.31\ g\ Pb(NO_3)_2$$

$$?\ g\ NaI = 0.0130\ mol\ PbI_2 \left(\frac{2\ mol\ NaI}{1\ mol\ PbI_2} \right) \left(\frac{149.9\ g\ NaI}{1\ mol\ NaI} \right) = 3.90\ g\ NaI$$

To carry out the reaction, we would dissolve each of these separately in water, and then mix the solutions. The lead(II) iodide precipitate would be filtered, dried, and weighed.

Suppose after carrying out this reaction, we isolated 4.77 g PbI_2. The percentage yield would be obtained as follows:

$$\%\ yield = \frac{actual\ yield}{theoretical\ yield} \times 100\% = \frac{4.77\ g}{6.00\ g} \times 100\% = 79.5\%$$

Notice that the theoretical yield is the mass of the lead(II) iodide we attempted to produce.

PRELAB QUESTIONS

1. Suppose you are asked to prepare 3.00 g of $BaSO_4$, an insoluble salt, by reacting $Ba(NO_3)_2$ (aq) with Na_2SO_4 (aq).
   (a) Write a balanced chemical equation for the reaction.
   (b) Calculate the mass of solid $Ba(NO_3)_2$ required.
   (c) Calculate the mass of solid Na_2SO_4 required.
2. Calculate the percentage yield if you performed the experiment described in question 1 and obtained 2.50 g $BaSO_4$.

EXPERIMENTAL

You will be asked to prepare one of the following substances: $BaCO_3$, $CaCO_3$, or $SrCO_3$. You will have the following materials available:

Materials
    calcium chloride, $CaCl_2$
    strontium nitrate, $Sr(NO_3)_2$
    barium chloride, $BaCl_2$
    potassium carbonate, K_2CO_3
    two 100 mL or 150 mL beakers
    one 250 mL beaker
    apparatus for gravity filtration

Time Required
    3 hours

LABORATORY NOTES

1. If you will be using a drying oven, set the oven temperature at about 100°C. If the oven temperature is too high, the filter paper will char.
2. If you are not yet familiar with gravity filtration, read the passage on this technique in the "Laboratory Equipment" section.

Cleaning Up
    General instructions for disposing of wastes generated in this experiment are provided at the end of each experimental procedure. Additional, more specific information and suggestions for managing hazardous wastes may be found in the *Instructor's Guide*. Your instructor will provide you with special waste handling directions when necessary.

PROCEDURE

1. Determine which of the chemicals provided could undergo reaction to produce the compound you have been assigned. Write a balanced equation. (If you are not sure of the solubilities of any of the reactants or products, consult a solubility table such as that provided in Appendix C of this manual.

2. Determine the number of moles of product you have been assigned to prepare. Then calculate the mass of each reactant required to prepare the desired quantity of product.
3. Weigh each reactant into a 100 mL or 150 mL beaker, and add 35 mL of distilled water. Stir each solution until the solute is completely dissolved. If the solute does not dissolve within 5 minutes, add an additional 10 mL of water, and continue to stir until the solute dissolves completely.
4. Mix the two solutions in a 250 mL beaker. Rinse each small beaker with a small amount of water, and add the rinsings to the large beaker. Allow the precipitate to form for at least 15 minutes. Stir the mixture frequently during this period.

EXPERIMENT
11

Determining the Molar Mass of a Volatile Liquid

PURPOSE

1. To determine the molar mass of a volatile substance.

DISCUSSION

In the course of investigating the structure of a compound, it is often helpful to know its molar mass. In this experiment, you will determine the molar mass of a volatile liquid by vaporizing a sample of the liquid in a flask that is immersed in a hot water bath. The volume, temperature, and pressure of the vapor will be determined, and the mass of the vapor will also be measured. By correcting the volume of the vapor to standard temperature and pressure (STP), the number of moles will provide the molar mass.

This technique is limited to substances that are easily vaporized. Several milliliters of the liquid to be vaporized will be placed in a 250 mL Erlenmeyer flask. A piece of aluminum foil will be crimped over the mouth of the flask to produce a tight cap. A small pinhole will be punched in the center of the aluminum foil cap to permit the escape of air and vapor. The flask will be placed in a hot water bath, and the unknown liquid allowed to vaporize. An excess of the liquid will be used, and as it vaporizes, the excess will escape from the flask, flushing the air that fills the flask initially. When vaporization is complete, the flask will be left with just enough vapor to fill it completely. Just prior to removal from the water bath, the vapor will be at the same temperature as the hot water bath. When the flask is removed from the bath and allowed to cool, the vapor left filling the flask will condense to its liquid form. The exterior of the flask will be dried, and the flask will be weighed.

If the flask is kept in boiling water after all of the liquid has vaporized, some of the unknown vapor will be replaced by air, resulting in an error in the mass measurement. Consequently, it is important to watch the flask carefully and remove it from the boiling water bath as soon as the liquid unknown has vaporized completely.

The mass of the vapor that fills the flask when it is removed from the hot water bath is obtained by subtracting the mass of the empty flask from the value obtained after the vapor has condensed. The volume of vapor in the flask can be determined by filling the flask to the very top with water and then measuring the volume of water with a large graduated cylinder. The temperature of the gas has been determined by measuring the temperature of the hot water bath when the flask was removed from the bath. Since the pressure of the gas is the same as the atmospheric pressure in the laboratory, the pressure can be measured by reading the barometer in the laboratory. From the accumulated information, it is possible to calculate the approximate molar mass of the unknown liquid used in the experiment.

Example. Suppose an empty 250 mL Erlenmeyer flask fitted with an aluminum foil cap has a mass of 35.73 g. After vaporization of a volatile liquid, as just described, the mass of the flask plus its contents is 36.87 g. The flask is filled to the very top with water, and the volume of water is found to be 263 mL. If the liquid was vaporized in a hot water bath at 97°C while the atmospheric pressure in the laboratory was 752 torr, what is the molar mass of the unknown liquid?

Solution. At STP, the volume of the vapor would be:

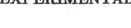

$$V_{STP} = 263 \text{ mL}\left(\frac{273 \text{ K}}{370 \text{ K}}\right)\left(\frac{752 \text{ torr}}{760 \text{ torr}}\right) = 192 \text{ mL}$$

At STP, one mole of a gas has a volume of 22.4 liters, so the number of moles of vapor is:

$$? \text{ mol} = 0.192 \text{ L}\left(\frac{1 \text{ mol}}{22.4 \text{ L}}\right) = 0.00857 \text{ mol}$$

To calculate the molar mass, the mass of vapor must be divided by the number of moles it equals. The mass of vapor is obtained by subtracting the mass of the empty flask from that of the flask filled with vapor:

$$36.87 \text{ g} - 35.73 \text{ g} = 1.14 \text{ g}$$

Division of the mass by the number of moles gives the molar mass:

$$\text{molar mass} = \frac{1.14 \text{ g}}{0.00857 \text{ mol}} = 133 \text{ g/mol}$$

PRELAB QUESTIONS

1. How many moles of gas are in a flask at 95°C and 748 torr if the total volume of the flask is 263 mL?
2. If the gas in question 1 has a mass of 1.23 g, what is its molar mass?
3. Which of the following liquids would not be suitable for molar mass determination by the method described in this experiment? Explain your answer.
   pentane, bp 36°C; acetic acid, bp 118°C; acetone, bp 56°C

EXPERIMENTAL

Materials
   250 mL Erlenmeyer flask
   1000 mL beaker

ring stand
iron ring
wire gauze
universal clamp
aluminum foil
barometer
500 mL graduated cylinder
volatile organic substances with boiling points below 100°C

Time Required
2 hours

Cleaning Up

General instructions for disposing of wastes generated in this experiment are provided at the end of each experimental procedure. Additional, more specific information and suggestions for managing hazardous wastes may be found in the *Instructor's Guide*. Your instructor will provide you with special waste handling directions when necessary.

PROCEDURE

Refer to Figure 12.1 as you prepare your laboratory set-up.

1. Obtain about 5 mL of an unknown liquid from your instructor. *a lot will evaporate*
2. Weigh a clean, dry 250 mL flask, together with a square of aluminum foil large enough to cover the mouth of the flask.
3. Lower the flask into a 1000 mL beaker. Hold the flask in place so that it does not float to the surface, and add water to the beaker outside of the flask so that the water level comes to the neck of the flask without filling it.
4. Remove the flask from the beaker, and heat the water in the beaker until it boils.
5. Have a thermometer handy on your bench before proceeding.
6. Pour about 65 mL of the unknown liquid into the Erlenmeyer flask and crimp the aluminum foil tightly over the mouth of the flask. Make a tiny pinhole in the center of the foil.
7. Attach a universal clamp to the neck of the flask. Using the clamp as a handle, immerse the flask in the beaker of water so that the neck is just above the water level. Tip the flask at as much of an angle as possible so the unknown liquid forms a pool in the bottom of the flask (Fig. 12.1). This will make it easier to see when the last of the liquid has vaporized than if the flask is held in a completely upright position.
8. Continue heating the water in the beaker until the liquid in the flask has almost vaporized completely. Then remove the Bunsen burner from the beaker. This will stop the boiling action of the water, making it easier to observe the final vaporization of the unknown liquid.
9. Watch the liquid carefully, and when you actually see the last of the liquid vaporize, remove the flask from the hot water bath. Measure the temperature of the water bath immediately.
10. Disconnect the universal clamp and dry the outside of the flask. Then, after allowing its contents to cool to room temperature, weigh the flask. The difference between this mass and that determined for the empty flask

represents the mass of the vapor that filled the flask at the moment it was removed from the hot water bath.

11. Carry out two more trials by adding another 6 mL of unknown liquid to the flask and repeating the procedure described in steps 6 – 10. It is not necessary to empty the residual unknown liquid between trials.

12. Read the barometer in the laboratory.

13. When you have completed all of your mass measurements, dry the inside of your Erlenmeyer flask. Then determine its total volume by filling it to the very top with tap water and measuring the volume of water with a 500 mL graduated cylinder.

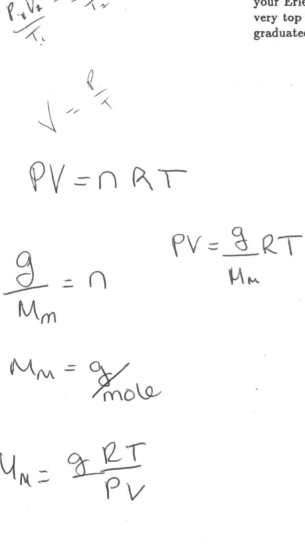

$$\frac{P_1 V_2}{T_1} = \frac{P_2 V_2}{T_2}$$

$$V = \frac{P}{T}$$

$$PV = nRT$$

$$\frac{g}{M_m} = n$$

$$M_m = g/mole$$

$$M_M = \frac{g\,RT}{PV}$$

$$PV = \frac{g}{M_M} RT$$

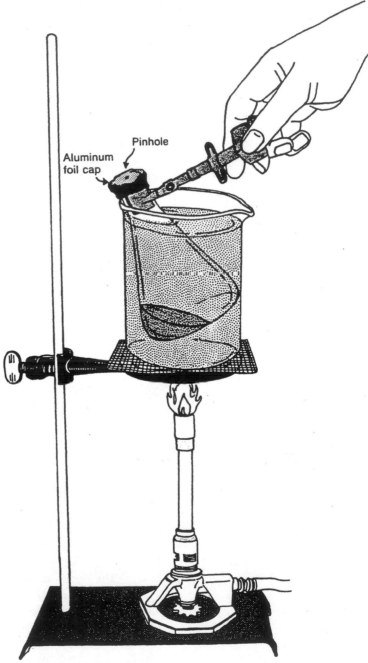

FIGURE 12.1
Apparatus for determining the molar mass of a volatile liquid.

Ionic Reactions

PURPOSE

1. To study the nature of ionic reactions.
2. To write net ionic equations for a series of precipitation reactions.

DISCUSSION

In this experiment, you will work with aqueous solutions of ionic substances. *Aqueous solutions* are those solutions in which water is the solvent. Water is a particularly good solvent for ionic solutes, because of its high polarity. When ionic substances are dissolved in water, the ions separate and become surrounded by water molecules (Fig. 8.1). This separation of ions is known as *dissociation*. Thus, when sodium chloride dissolves in water, the resulting solution contains aqueous sodium ions, $Na^+(aq)$, and aqueous chloride ions, $Cl^-(aq)$:

$$NaCl(s) \xrightarrow[\text{in water}]{\text{dissolves}} Na^+(aq) + Cl^-(aq)$$

The symbols (s) and (aq) in this equation are known as *state symbols*, and they refer to the *solid* and *aqueous* states, respectively. State symbols are useful when we wish to be specific about the condition of a substance. In this experiment, it will be necessary to specify such conditions. In your study of chemistry, you will also encounter the state symbols (l) and (g) that correspond to the *liquid* and *gaseous* states, respectively.

Rather than write the formulas of individual ions, the formula $NaCl(aq)$ may be used to represent an aqueous sodium chloride solution. Similarly, an aqueous barium nitrate solution, $Ba(NO_3)_2\ (aq)$, contains aqueous barium ions and aqueous nitrate ions:

$$Ba(NO_3)_2(aq) = Ba^{2+}(aq) + 2\ NO_3^-(aq)$$

Let us suppose we have two aqueous solutions, one containing silver nitrate, $AgNO_3(aq)$, and the other containing sodium chloride, $NaCl(aq)$. The

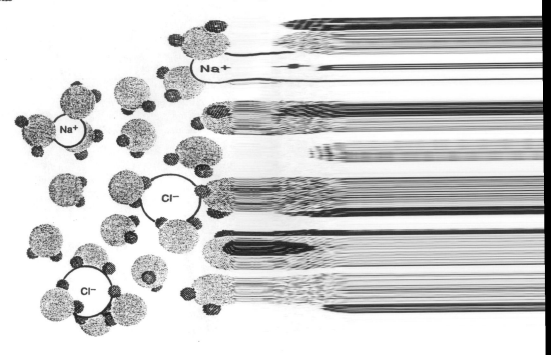

FIGURE 8.1
When an ionic substance dissolves, the ion———————
and are surrounded by water molecules.

ions present in the two solutions are as follow———————

Solution 1: Ag^+ and NO_3^-

Solution 2: Na^+ and Cl^-

If the two solutions are mixed, a n———————
formation of an insoluble solid. Since the **t** ———————
newly formed substance must be the **result** ———————
solid product such as this is known as a *pr*———————
of reaction a precipitation reaction.

Precipitates are electrically uncharge———————
cipitates result from the exchange of positiv———————
solutions of two ionic compounds. Thus, **i**———————
be either silver chloride, AgCl, or sodium **ni**———————

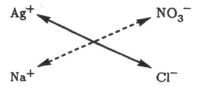

Sodium nitrate dissolves readily in water an———————
conclude that silver chloride is the insolu**bl**———————
formation of this precipitate as follows:

$$Ag^+ (aq) + Cl^- (aq) \rightarrow AgCl (s)$$

EXPERIMENT
12

Ionic Reactions

1. To study the nature of ionic reactions.
2. To write net ionic equations for a series of precipitation reactions.

In this experiment, you will work with aqueous solutions of ionic substances. *Aqueous solutions* are those solutions in which water is the solvent. Water is a particularly good solvent for ionic solutes, because of its high polarity. When ionic substances are dissolved in water, the ions separate and become surrounded by water molecules (Fig. 8.1). This separation of ions is known as *dissociation*. Thus, when sodium chloride dissolves in water, the resulting solution contains aqueous sodium ions, $Na^+(aq)$, and aqueous chloride ions, $Cl^-(aq)$:

$$NaCl(s) \xrightarrow[\text{in water}]{\text{dissolves}} Na^+(aq) + Cl^-(aq)$$

The symbols (s) and (aq) in this equation are known as *state symbols*, and they refer to the *solid* and *aqueous* states, respectively. State symbols are useful when we wish to be specific about the condition of a substance. In this experiment, it will be necessary to specify such conditions. In your study of chemistry, you will also encounter the state symbols (l) and (g) that correspond to the *liquid* and *gaseous* states, respectively.

Rather than write the formulas of individual ions, the formula $NaCl(aq)$ may be used to represent an aqueous sodium chloride solution. Similarly, an aqueous barium nitrate solution, $Ba(NO_3)_2 (aq)$, contains aqueous barium ions and aqueous nitrate ions:

$$Ba(NO_3)_2(aq) = Ba^{2+}(aq) + 2 NO_3^-(aq)$$

Let us suppose we have two aqueous solutions, one containing silver nitrate, $AgNO_3(aq)$, and the other containing sodium chloride, $NaCl(aq)$. The

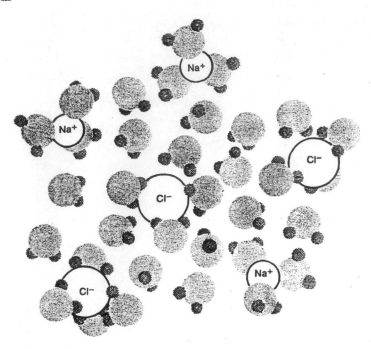

FIGURE 8.1
When an ionic substance dissolves, the ions become separated from one another and are surrounded by water molecules.

ions present in the two solutions are as follows:

Solution 1: Ag^+ and NO_3^-

Solution 2: Na^+ and Cl^-

If the two solutions are mixed, a milkiness will appear, caused by the formation of an insoluble solid. Since the two solutions were clear initially, this newly formed substance must be the result of a chemical change. An insoluble solid product such as this is known as a *precipitate* (ppt), and we call this type of reaction a precipitation reaction.

Precipitates are electrically uncharged. In this experiment, all of the precipitates result from the exchange of positive and negative ions between reacting solutions of two ionic compounds. Thus, in our example, the precipitate must be either silver chloride, AgCl, or sodium nitrate, $NaNO_3$.

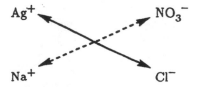

Sodium nitrate dissolves readily in water and is therefore soluble. Thus we can conclude that silver chloride is the insoluble precipitate. We can represent the formation of this precipitate as follows:

$$Ag^+ (aq) + Cl^- (aq) \rightarrow AgCl (s)$$

The equation is interpreted to mean that aqueous silver ions combine wi aqueous chloride ions to form a solid precipitate of silver chloride.

Precipitates do not always form in a 1:1 ratio of ions. For exampl addition of aqueous silver nitrate, $AgNO_3$ (aq), to aqueous sodium sulfid $Na_2S(aq)$, also produces a precipitate:

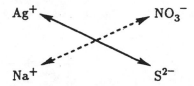

Since sodium nitrate is soluble, the precipitate must be silver sulfide. The pr cipitate forms from the simplest ratio of ions to give an uncharged formula:

$$2\,Ag^+\,(aq) + S^{2-}\,(aq)\ \rightarrow\ Ag_2S\,(s)$$

The two ionic equations we have just shown are called *net ionic equ tions.* In each of the reactions, sodium and nitrate ions were present, but neith actually was involved in the reaction. Ions that are present but do not get i volved in the reaction are called *spectator ions.* Thus, the net ionic equati shows the "net" reaction that takes place, leaving out the spectator ions.

In this experiment, you will be asked to use the data from several comb nations of solutions to determine which combinations have resulted precipitation. A very important principle that will help you to eliminate certa combinations is the following: *If a given pair of positive and negative ions a observed together in any solution without forming a precipitate, then they w never precipitate together.* For example, no precipitate forms when NaCl(a and $KNO_3(aq)$ are mixed:

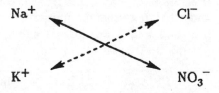

From this, we can conclude that sodium chloride, potassium chloride, sodiu nitrate, and potassium nitrate are all soluble in water. Our principle al implies that *any soluble ionic substance will never be observed as a precipitate.*

In this experiment, you will work with five sets of solutions. Each s contains six solutions. For each set you will mix all possible combinations the six solutions. By analyzing the combinations of solutions that produce p cipitates and the ones that do not, you will determine the pairs of ions th combine as precipitates, and write net ionic equations for all reactions th occur. The sets must be done in numerical order, since you occasionally w need data gathered in one of the previous sets. The following example provided to clarify the logic you will use.

Example. Suppose all possible combinations of the following solutions (sol are mixed:

Solution 1: KNO_3, which contains K^+ and NO_3^-

Solution 2: $Pb(NO_3)_2$, which contains Pb^{2+} and NO_3^-

Solution 3: $BaCl_2$, which contains Ba^{2+} and Cl^-

Solution 4: K_2CO_3, which contains K^+ and CO_3^{2-}

The following table shows the results that would be obtained:

	Soln 4: K^+/CO_3^{2-}	Soln 3: Ba^{2+}/Cl^-	Soln 2: Pb^{2+}/NO_3^-	Soln 1: K^+/NO_3^-
Soln 1: K^+/NO_3^-	no change	no change	no change	
Soln 2: Pb^{2+}/NO_3^-	ppt A	ppt B		
Soln 3: Ba^{2+}/Cl^-	ppt C			
Soln 4: K^+/CO_3^{2-}				

Determine the identity of precipitates A, B, and C, and write a net ionic equation for the formation of each.

Solution.   Precipitate A may come from the combination of K^+ and NO_3^- or of Pb^{2+} and CO_3^{2-}. It cannot be from K^+ and NO_3^-, since these they are together in solution 1, KNO_3. Thus, precipitate A must arise from:

$$Pb^{2+}(aq) + CO_3^{2-}(aq) \rightarrow PbCO_3(s)$$

Precipitate B may come from a combination of Ba^{2+} and NO_3^- or from Pb^{2+} and Cl^-. It cannot be from Ba^{2+} and NO_3^-, since these are together when solutions 1 and 3 are mixed, and no precipitate forms in that mixture. Thus, precipitate B must arise from:

$$Pb^{2+}(aq) + 2\, Cl^-(aq) \rightarrow PbCl_2(s)$$

Precipitate C may come from a combination of Ba^{2+} and CO_3^{2-} or from K^+ and Cl^-. It cannot be from K^+ and Cl^-, since these are together when solutions 1 and 3 are mixed, and no precipitate is observed in that mixture. Thus, precipitate C must arise from:

$$Ba^{2+}(aq) + CO_3^{2-}(aq) \rightarrow BaCO_3(s)$$

PRELAB QUESTIONS

1. Write a balanced net ionic equation for each of the following pairs of ions that form precipitates.
   (a) Cu^{2+} and S^{2-}
   (b) Pb^{2+} and Br^-
   (c) Hg^{2+} and PO_4^{3-}
2. Sodium iodide, NaI, and potassium nitrate, KNO_3, are both soluble in water. What will happen when an aqueous solution of sodium nitrate, $NaNO_3$, is mixed with an aqueous solution of potassium iodide, KI? Explain your answer.

3. Silver iodide, AgI, is an insoluble solid. Referring to the information given in questiom 2, predict what will happen when an aqueous solution of silver nitrate, $AgNO_3$, is mixed with aqueous potassium iodide, KI.

EXPERIMENTAL

Materials

acetate sheets or test tubes
five sets of ionic solutions as follows:

	Set I	Set II	Set III	Set IV	Set V
Solution 1:	$Ba(NO_3)_2$	Na_2SO_4	$FeCl_3$	$NiCl_2$	$BaCl_2$
Solution 2:	$BaCl_2$	$Al_2(SO_4)_3$	$Co(NO_3)_2$	$MgCl_2$	$Sr(NO_3)_2$
Solution 3:	Na_2CrO_4	$Sr(NO_3)_2$	$CoCl_2$	K_2SO_4	Na_2CrO_4
Solution 4:	K_2CrO_4	$BaCl_2$	$NaOH$	$NaOH$	$Al_2(SO_4)_3$
Solution 5:	$NaNO_3$	$Ba(NO_3)_2$	KOH	$Ba(OH)_2$	K_2CrO_4
Solution 6:	KCl	$AlCl_3$	$NaNO_3$	$MgSO_4$	$AgNO_3$

Time Required
3 hours

LABORATORY NOTES

1. When solutions of $Ba(OH)_2$ and $NaOH$ are mixed in set IV, a precipitate of barium carbonate may result if carbon dioxide is dissolved in the sodium hydroxide. The reaction that takes place is the following:

$$Ba(OH)_2(aq) + CO_2(aq) \rightarrow BaCO_3(s) + H_2O(l)$$

If you observe this result, ignore it. No reaction will occur if carbon dioxide is absent.

2. Avoid getting silver nitrate ($AgNO_3$) on your skin. It will leave a dark stain that takes about a week to fade.

Cleaning Up

General instructions for disposing of wastes generated in this experiment are provided at the end of each experimental procedure. Additional, more specific information and suggestions for managing hazardous wastes may be found in the *Instructor's Guide*. Your instructor will provide you with special waste handling directions when necessary.

PROCEDURE

1. You will be given five sets of ionic solutions, with each set containing six solutions. Use the data tables at the end of this section to organize your work. For each set of solutions, mix all possible combinations two at a time (for example, mix 1 and 2, 1 and 3, 1 and 4, 1 and 5, and so forth). This can be accomplished most readily by mixing a drop of each on an acetate sheet having a grid like the following:

	Soln 6	Soln 5	Soln 4	Soln 3	Soln 2
Soln 1	mix 1 & 6 here	mix 1 & 5 here	mix 1 & 4 here	and so forth . . .	
Soln 2					
Soln 3					
Soln 4					
Soln 5					

(If acetate sheets are not available, you must use a test tube for each combination.)

2. Note any precipitates that form.
3. After all possible combinations have been mixed for set I, determine the formula of each precipitate formed, and write a net ionic equation for the reaction. Remember, a given combination of two ions can be eliminated as a precipitate if one of the solutions in any of the sets is made up of those ions, or if the two ions were mixed together in one of the mixtures that did not result in a precipitate. It is necessary to work with the five sets in numerical order, since determination of precipitates in later sets frequently depends on information gathered in the earlier sets. Complete each set before proceeding to the next.

Cleaning Up

After you complete each set of solutions, use your distilled water wash bottle to rinse the drops off of the acetate sheet into the waste container provided for this purpose. Dry the acetate sheet with a paper towel.

REPORT SHEET — Experiment 12

Ionic Reactions

Set I

	K^+/Cl^-	Na^+/NO_3^-	K^+/CrO_4^{2-}	Na^+/CrO_4^{2-}	Ba^{2+}/Cl^-
Ba^{2+}/NO_3^-					
Ba^{2+}/Cl^-					
Na^+/CrO_4^{2-}					
K^+/CrO_4^{2-}					
Na^+/NO_3^-					

Net ionic equations:

NAME: ____________________ DATE: __________

Report Sheet — Experiment 12 (continued)

Set II

	Al^{3+}/Cl^-	Ba^{2+}/NO_3^-	Ba^{2+}/Cl^-	Sr^{2+}/NO_3^-	Al^{3+}/SO_4^{2-}
Na^+/SO_4^{2-}					
Al^{3+}/SO_4^{2-}					
Sr^{2+}/NO_3^-					
Ba^{2+}/Cl^-					
Ba^{2+}/NO_3^-					

Net ionic equations:

Set III

	Na^+/NO_3^-	K^+/OH^-	Na^+/OH^-	Co^{2+}/Cl^-	Co^{2+}/NO_3^-
Fe^{3+}/Cl^-					
Co^{2+}/NO_3^-					
Co^{2+}/Cl^-					
Na^+/OH^-					
K^+/OH^-					

Report Sheet — Experiment 12 (continued)

Net ionic equations:

Set IV

	Mg^{2+}/SO_4^{2-}	Ba^{2+}/OH^-	Na^+/OH^-	K^+/SO_4^{2-}	Mg^{2+}/Cl^-
Ni^{2+}/Cl^-					
Mg^{2+}/Cl^-					
K^+/SO_4^{2-}					
Na^+/OH^-		*			
Ba^{2+}/OH^-					

*See Laboratory Notes.

Net ionic equations:

Report Sheet — Experiment 12 (continued)

Set V

	Ag^+/NO_3^-	K^+/CrO_4^{2-}	Al^{3+}/SO_4^{2-}	Na^+/CrO_4^{2-}	Sr^{2+}/NO_3^-
Ba^{2+}/Cl^-					
Sr^{2+}/NO_3^-					
Na^+/CrO_4^{2-}					
Al^{3+}/SO_4^{2-}					
K^+/CrO_4^{2-}					

Net ionic equations:

Questions — Experiment 12

1. Use the information you have gathered to fill in the following solubility chart as shown. Place an *S* (soluble) in the grid for combinations of ions that do not precipitate, and an *I* (insoluble) for those that do (Several compounds that you will not have enough information to determine have been filled in to help you complete the table.) Check your observations in the *Handbook of Chemistry and Physics* or Appendix E o *Introductory Chemistry* by Krimsley.

	Cl^-	CrO_4^{2-}	NO_3^-	OH^-	SO_4^{2-}
Ag^+				—	I^*
Al^{3+}				I	
K^+					
Mg^{2+}		S	S		
Na^+					
Sr^{2+}				S	

*Silver sulfate is frequently classified as "slightly soluble," since it has a solubility of about 0.1 g/100 mL in water.

2. Referring to the table you have just prepared, what generalization can you make about the solubility o compounds containing:

(a) The nitrate ion?

(b) The sodium ion?

(c) The potassium ion?

EXPERIMENT
13

Titration of Hydrochloric Acid and Sodium Hydroxide

PURPOSE

1. To learn to prepare a dilute solution.
2. To recognize a titration endpoint.
3. To calculate Molarity (M) and the Average Molarity (M).

DISCUSSION

Since the Titration Equation is:

$$1\ HCl\ +\ 1\ NaOH \quad NaCl + 1\ H_2O$$

it follows that the Titration Equivalence Point (i.e. approximate end point) the number of moles of Hydrochloric acid (HCl) is equal to the number of moles of Sodium hydroxide (NaOH).

Since:

$$(Molarity) \cdot (Volume)\ =\ moles$$

it follows that at the equivalence point:

$$M_{HCl} \cdot V_{HCl} = M_{NaOH} \cdot V_{NaOH}$$

 © 2001 D. Cody and E. Shenal

For this titration you will assume that the exact Molarity of HCl is 0.1M. The Molarity of NaOH will therefore be experimentally determined.

EXPERIMENTAL

Materials
  2 500-mL burets
  250-mL Erlenmeyer flask
  500-mL Erlenmeyer flask
  6M Hydrochloric acid (HCl)
  6M Sodium Hydroxide (NaOH)
  0.1 % Phenolphthalein

Time Required
  2 ½ hours

Cleaning Up
  Follow the instructions provided by your instructor.

PROCEDURE

1. **Preparation of Approximately 0.1 Hydrochloric acid (HCl)**
   Using a **500**-mL graduated cylinder measure approximately **295**-mL of distilled water and place it in a 500-mL Erlenmeyer flask. Using a 1 mL graduated cylinder measure out approximately **5**-mL of 6M HCl and add it to the 295-mL of water. In order to insure uniform solution concentration, the H_2O/HCl mixture should be agitated for at least three minutes.

2. **Preparation of Approximately 0.1 Sodium hydroxide (NaOH).**
   Using a **500**-mL graduated cylinder measure approximately **295**-mL of distilled water and place it in a 500-mL Erlenmeyer flask. Using a **10**-mL graduated cylinder measure out approximately **5**-mL of 6M NaOH and add it to the 295-mL of water. In order to insure uniform solution concentration, the $H_2O/NaOH$ mixture should be agitated for at least three minutes.

3. **Buret Preparation**
   Thoroughly clean and rinse two burets with distilled water. Then rinse one buret three times with 5-mL of 0.1M HCl. Fill the buret with fresh 0.1M HCl. Repeat the procedure with the second buret using 0.1M NaOH.

4. **HCl Buret**
   Using the HCl buret place **5.00**-mL of 0.1M HCl in a **250** ml Erlenmeyer flask and add approximately 50-mL of distilled water and 2-3 drops of *Phenolphthalein* Indicator.

5. **NaOH Buret**
   From the NaOH buret add NaOH solution dropwise, with mixing, until the solution in the flask turns **very light pink** (the pink must be permanent).

Record the buret volume of NaOH required to create a permanent pink color to ± 0.05-mL.

6. Repeat the Titration (Steps 4 and 5) nine more times.

7. **Calculations**
   a) Subtract the Initial NaOH Buret Reading from the Final NaOH Buret reading to determine the volume of NaOH for each trial.
   b) Calculate the Molarity of NaOH for each trial
   c) Determine the Average Molarity of NaOH

REPORT SHEET — EXPERIMENT 13 – TITRATION

Show any calculations in the spaces provided.

BURET DATA

Trial	Volume mL HCl	Final NaOH Buret Reading	Initial NaOH Buret Reading	Volume mL NaOH	Molarity (M) NaOH
1	5.00		0.00 mL		
2	5.00				
3	5.00				
4	5.00				
5	5.00				
6	5.00				
7	5.00				
8	5.00				
9	5.00				
10	5.00				
				Average Molarity NaOH	

QUESTIONS — EXPERIMENT 13 – TITRATION

Show all work and include units in all problems.

1. What is the Molarity (M) of a solution prepared by diluting 55-mL of 0.65 M Hydrochloric acid (HCl) solution to a final volume of 155-mL by adding water?

2. How much water, in milliliters, must be added to 60.0-mL of 3.30 M Sodium chloride (NaCl) solution to decrease its concentration to 0.0225 M?

3. What are the sources of error in this experiment?

WORKSHEET 1

MISC 490

modular • laboratory • program • in • chemistry

program editor: Conrad L. Stanitski

Using Exponential Notation and Significant Figures

prepared by **Norman E. Griswold**, Nebraska Wesleyan University

Purpose of the Experiment

Review exponential notation and use it to solve problems with and without a calculator. Review rules for determining significant figures and use them to round off calculations.

Background Information

I. Exponential Notation

During your study of chemistry, you will encounter numbers ranging from the incredibly large to the extremely small. For example, a 100-mL sample of water contains more than 3 septillion molecules of water, or 3,000,000,000,000,000,000,000,000 molecules. Each water molecule has a mass of approximately 30 septillionths of a gram, or 0.000 000 000 000 000 000 000 03 grams. Representing very large or very small numbers this way is awkward and time consuming. Consequently, we usually use exponential notation, sometimes called **scientific notation**, to express such numbers.

A. Expressing Numbers Using Exponential Notation

Exponential notation expresses numbers as the product of two factors. The first factor, the **digit term**, is a number between 1 and 10. The digit term is multiplied by the second factor, called the **exponential term**, which has the form 10^x, 10 raised to a specific whole number power called the **exponent**.

For example, using exponential notation we represent 126 as 1.26×10^2, which we read as "one point two six times ten to the second". As shown in Figure 1, the digit term in this expression is 1.26. This term includes all the significant figures of the number being represented. (We will review the rules for determining significant figures in Part II of this module.)

$$1.26 \times 10^2 \leftarrow \text{exponent}$$

digit term ↗ ↖ exponential term

Figure 1 *Exponential notation*

The exponential term in this example is 10^2. A positive exponent represents the number of times the digit term must be ***multiplied*** by 10 to give the number represented. For example, 1.26×10^2 means $1.26 \times 10 \times 10 = 126$. Note that there are three figures in the digit term and three figures in the number being represented.

Some additional examples of numbers expressed in exponential notation are:

$$273.15 = 2.7315 \times 10^2$$
$$0.08206 = 8.206 \times 10^{-2}$$
$$0.001 = 1 \times 10^{-3}$$

These examples show that, when expressed using exponential notation, numbers greater than 10 have positive exponents and numbers less than 1 have negative exponents.

A negative exponent represents the number of times the digit term must be *divided* by 10 to give the number being represented. Thus, 2.46×10^{-3} means

$$2.46 \times \frac{1}{10} \times \frac{1}{10} \times \frac{1}{10} = 0.00246$$

Another way to interpret the exponent is to say that the exponent is equal to the number of places we must move the decimal point in a number to convert the number into the digit term. If the decimal point must be moved to the *left*, the exponent is positive. For example, the number 126 can be expressed as 1.26×10^2. The decimal point (following the 6 in 126) must be moved two places to the left to give the digit term, 1.26, so the exponent is a positive 2.

If the decimal point must be moved to the *right*, the exponent is negative. As another example, 0.00246 can be expressed as 2.46×10^{-3}. The exponential term is 10^{-3}, because the decimal point in 0.00246 must be moved three places to the right to give the digit term, 2.46. We could also express 0.00246 as 24.6×10^{-4}, 246×10^{-5}, or even as 0.246×10^{-2}. However, scientists usually keep the digit term between 1 and 10. For this example then, 2.46×10^{-3} is preferred, although the other expressions are acceptable.

B. Exponential Notation Using a Calculator

An electronic calculator is an important aid for performing chemical calculations. Your calculator may be slightly different from the one used for the following examples. If so, use your calculator's instruction book when performing these tasks.

To use exponential notation with your calculator, it must have an exponent key, usually labeled ⟦EXP⟧ (or ⟦EE⟧ or ⟦EEX⟧ on some models).

1. Entering Exponential Numbers on a Calculator   To enter 1.26×10^2 on a calculator with an ⟦EXP⟧ key, press the following keys in the order shown.

$$\boxed{1}\ \boxed{\cdot}\ \boxed{2}\ \boxed{6}\ \boxed{EXP}\ \boxed{2}$$

To enter 2.46×10^{-3} on a calculator with an ⟦EXP⟧ key, press the following keys in order.

$$\boxed{2}\ \boxed{\cdot}\ \boxed{4}\ \boxed{6}\ \boxed{EXP}\ \boxed{+/-}\ \boxed{3}$$

The ⟦+/−⟧ key may be labeled ⟦CHS⟧ for "change sign".

Some calculators can be set so that the answers are automatically expressed in exponential notation on the display. If your calculator has the appropriate keys, select the exponential notation mode by pressing ⟦2nd⟧, then ⟦SCI⟧. Other calculators require different keystrokes to select the exponential notation mode.

The following example shows the different answers obtained using the normal mode and the exponential notation mode.

normal mode: $(3.2 \times 10^{-3}) \times (5 \times 10^{-4}) = 0.0000016$

exponential notation mode: $(3.2 \times 10^{-3}) \times (5 \times 10^{-4})$
$$= 1.6 \times 10^{-6}$$

2. Adding, Subtracting, Multiplying, and Dividing Exponential Expressions   In order to use a calculator to add, subtract, multiply, or divide exponential expressions, we use the keys ⟦+⟧, ⟦−⟧, ⟦×⟧, or ⟦÷⟧, which represent these operations, just as we would when manipulating numbers in normal notation. The only difference is that you must first select exponential notation mode. For example, use the following sequence of keystrokes to calculate $(3.2 \times 10^{-3}) \times (5 \times 10^{-4})$.

$$\boxed{3}\boxed{\cdot}\boxed{2}\boxed{EXP}\boxed{+/-}\boxed{3}\boxed{\times}\boxed{5}\boxed{EXP}\boxed{+/-}\boxed{4}\boxed{=} = 1.6 \times 10^{-6}$$

3. Determining Square Roots and Cube Roots of Exponential Expressions   To obtain square roots of exponential numbers, remember that $\sqrt{A} = A^{1/2}$ and use the ⟦√x⟧ or ⟦y^x⟧ key. For calculators with a ⟦y^x⟧ key, use the following sequence of keystrokes to find the square root of 2.7×10^{10}.

$$\boxed{2}\boxed{\cdot}\boxed{7}\boxed{EXP}\boxed{1}\boxed{0}\boxed{y^x}\boxed{\cdot}\boxed{5}\boxed{=} = 1.6 \times 10^5$$

The ⟦·⟧ and ⟦5⟧ keystrokes are used because ½ = 0.5.

To obtain cube roots of exponential numbers, remember that $\sqrt[3]{A} = A^{1/3} = A^{0.333}$, and use the ⟦$y^x$⟧ key. For example, to take the cube root of 2.7×10^{10}, use the following sequence of keystrokes.

$$\boxed{2}\boxed{\cdot}\boxed{7}\boxed{EXP}\boxed{1}\boxed{0}\boxed{y^x}\boxed{\cdot}\boxed{3}\boxed{3}\boxed{3}\boxed{=} = 2.97 \times 10^3$$

4. Taking Logarithms and Antilogs of Exponential Numbers   A logarithm is an exponent: It is the power to which 10 must be raised in order to produce a given number. For example, $1.5 \times 10^4 = 10^{4.18}$. The given number is 1.5×10^4, and its logarithm is 4.18. The logarithm of 1.5×10^4, written as $\log 1.5 \times 10^4$, can be determined by the following sequence of keystrokes.

$$\boxed{1}\boxed{\cdot}\boxed{5}\boxed{EXP}\boxed{4}\boxed{\log} = 4.18$$

150

The reverse of obtaining ("taking") a logarithm is taking the antilog. To take the antilog of 4.18, select the exponential notation mode on your calculator. Then use the following keystrokes to calculate antilog $10^{4.18}$.

$$\boxed{1}\,\boxed{0}\,\boxed{y^x}\,\boxed{4}\,\boxed{\bullet}\,\boxed{1}\,\boxed{8}\,\boxed{=} = 1.5 \times 10^4$$

If your calculator is not set for exponential notation mode, the answer will appear as 15135.612.

C. Using Exponential Numbers without a Calculator

1. Adding and Subtracting Exponential Numbers To add or subtract exponential numbers without a calculator, the numbers must have the same exponents. Consider the following example: $(1.27 \times 10^3) + (4 \times 10^1)$. One way to express these numbers so that they have identical exponents is to rewrite 4×10^1 as 0.04×10^3. Moving the decimal point two places to the left increases the exponent by two. The example then becomes $(1.27 \times 10^3) + (0.04 \times 10^3)$. Next, add the digit terms, the sum of which becomes the digit term of the answer. The final answer is the answer digit term multiplied by the common exponential term, as shown.

$$
\begin{array}{rcl}
1.27 \times 10^3 & \longrightarrow & 1.27 \times 10^3 \\
+\ \underline{4 \times 10^1} & \longrightarrow & +\ \underline{0.04 \times 10^3} \\
& & 1.31 \times 10^3
\end{array}
$$

The following is the result if we rewrite 1.27×10^3, rather than 4×10^1, before adding.

$$
\begin{array}{rcl}
1.27 \times 10^3 & \longrightarrow & 127 \times 10^1 \\
+\ \underline{4 \times 10^1} & \longrightarrow & +\ \underline{4 \times 10^1} \\
& & 131 \times 10^1 = 1.31 \times 10^3
\end{array}
$$

The answer is the same: It does not matter which number we change before addition. However, the first method directly gives the result in preferred exponential form (only one digit to the left of the decimal point).

The rules for subtraction of exponential numbers are the same as for addition, except that the digit terms are subtracted rather than added. Here are two examples:

$$
\begin{array}{rcl}
1.0 \times 10^2 & \longrightarrow & 10 \times 10^1 \\
-\ \underline{4 \times 10^1} & \longrightarrow & -\ \underline{4 \times 10^1} \\
& & 6 \times 10^1
\end{array}
$$

$$
\begin{array}{rcl}
3.2 \times 10^{-3} & \longrightarrow & 3.2 \times 10^{-3} \\
-\ \underline{5 \times 10^{-4}} & \longrightarrow & -\ \underline{0.5 \times 10^{-3}} \\
& & 2.7 \times 10^{-3}
\end{array}
$$

2. Multiplying Exponential Numbers When multiplying or dividing exponential numbers without a calculator, it is not necessary for the numbers to have identical exponents. To multiply exponential numbers, first multiply the digit terms. Then **add** the exponents to obtain the exponential term of the answer. A general expression for this procedure is:

$$(A \times 10^n)(B \times 10^m) = (A \times B) \times 10^{n+m}$$

Here are some specific examples:

$$(2 \times 10^4)(4 \times 10^2) = (2 \times 4) \times 10^{4+2} = 8 \times 10^6$$

$$(2 \times 10^4)(4 \times 10^{-2}) = (2 \times 4) \times 10^{4+(-2)} = 8 \times 10^2$$

$$(2 \times 10^{-4})(4 \times 10^{-2}) = (2 \times 4) \times 10^{(-4)+(-2)} = 8 \times 10^{-6}$$

Sometimes multiplying exponential numbers results in an answer in which the exponential term is 10^0. In such cases, remember that $10^0 = 1$ exactly; the exponential term can be dropped from the answer. For example:

$$(2 \times 10^4)(4 \times 10^{-4}) = (2 \times 4) \times 10^{4+(-4)} = 8 \times 10^0 = 8$$

3. Dividing Exponential Numbers To divide exponential numbers, first divide the digit terms. Then **subtract** the exponent of the denominator from the exponent of the numerator to obtain the exponent of the answer. A general expression of this procedure is:

$$\frac{A \times 10^n}{B \times 10^m} = \frac{A}{B} \times 10^{n-m}$$

Some specific examples are:

$$\frac{6 \times 10^4}{3 \times 10^2} = \frac{6}{3} \times 10^{4-2} = 2 \times 10^2$$

$$\frac{6 \times 10^4}{3 \times 10^{-2}} = \frac{6}{3} \times 10^{4-(-2)} = 2 \times 10^6$$

$$\frac{6 \times 10^{-4}}{3 \times 10^{-2}} = \frac{6}{3} \times 10^{(-4)-(-2)} = 2 \times 10^{-2}$$

Problem Set 1

(Use the spaces provided for the answers and additional paper if necessary.)

1. Some numbers of interest to chemists are given below. Express each number in proper exponential notation.

(a) 96,485 C (the Faraday constant)

(b) 299,792,458 m/s (speed of light in a vacuum)

(c) 0.0000000128 cm (radius of a metallic copper atom)

(d) 0.000001315 m (wavelength of an iodine laser)

2. Solve the following problems and express your answer in proper exponential notation. Try doing (a)–(d) without a calculator, first. Then do them with a calculator.

(a) $(3.8 \times 10^{-4}) + (4.000 \times 10^{-2}) =$

(b) $(2.40 \times 10^{6}) - (4 \times 10^{4}) =$

(c) $(2.10 \times 10^{8})(3.00 \times 10^{-14}) =$

(d) $\dfrac{7.69 \times 10^{6}}{2.00 \times 10^{-2}} =$

(e) $\left(\dfrac{2.73 \times 10^{-6}}{5.46 \times 10^{4}}\right) \div (1.00 \times 10^{-3}) =$

(f) $\left(\dfrac{2.40 \times 10^{-6}}{1.20 \times 10^{4}}\right) + (3.48 \times 10^{-8}) =$

name   section   date

152

II. Significant Figures

One of the first concepts taught in chemistry is **density**, the mass of a substance divided by its volume. Suppose that, to help understand density, you are asked to determine the density of a metal sample as accurately as possible. Using an analytical balance, you determine the mass of the assigned metal sample as 14.3216 g. If its volume is 2.00 mL, what should you report as the density of the metal?

When more than 100 students were asked this question, they gave the following answers: 7.1608 (most common), 7.160, 7.161, 7.16, 7.1, 7.2, and "about 7." Are all these answers correct? If not, which is correct? Would these answers have differed if the mass had been reported as 14 g? How can you report experimental results in a way that indicates the exactness of the measurements involved? All these questions can be resolved by using some simple rules to determine the proper number of figures to use when reporting a result obtained from measurements. The proper number of figures to include are called **significant figures** or **significant numbers**.

The basic rule for determining significant figures is: **only those figures that are reasonably reliable are significant**. The following sections describe how to determine which figures in a measurement are reasonably reliable and, therefore, are significant figures.

A. Kinds of Experimental Values

Experimental values in chemistry consist of two broad groups: **exact numbers** and **inexact numbers**. The first group includes numbers that arise from counting or from certain definitions. For example, if we count the students in a chemistry class, we know the exact number of people in the class. Similarly, some numerical relationships are exact by definition. Such numbers can be thought of as having an infinite number of significant figures. Some examples include:

$$1.000 \text{ L} = 1000 \text{ mL}$$
$$1.000 \text{ cm} = 1.00 \times 10^7 \text{ nm}$$
$$1.00 \text{ g} = 1.00 \times 10^{-3} \text{ kg}$$

By definition, 1.000 liter is **exactly** equal to 1000 milliliters. These examples are all conversions within a given system of units, in this case, the metric system.

The second group, inexact numbers, consists of numbers resulting from measurements and approximate conversion factors. The exactness of a measurement depends upon the measuring device. For example, Figure 2 shows arrows positioned at identical locations on three scales that differ only in the number of measuring marks. In Figure 2(a), the estimated position of the arrow is 6 or 7. A more exact position cannot be obtained using the scale in Figure 2(a). Figure 2(b) shows that the arrow is slightly closer to 7 than to 6. Using the scale in Figure 2(b), we can estimate that the arrow is at 6.5 or 6.6. The scale in Figure 2(c) makes it clear that the arrow is closer to 6.6 than to 6.5. Using the scale in Figure 2(c), a reasonable estimate for the arrow position is about 6.58 or 6.59. As you can see, the exactness of a measurement depends on the measuring device.

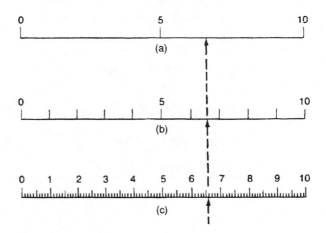

Figure 2 *Examples of measurement using scales of varying precision*

Certain conversion factors are also inexact. This situation occurs when converting from one system of units to another system, such as converting from the English system to the metric system. For example, by definition, the conversion of the mass unit called the English pound to the metric kilogram is:

$$1.00 \text{ lb} = 0.45359237 \text{ kg}$$

However, a more common (but less exact) conversion factor found in many tables is:

$$1 \text{ lb} = 0.4536 \text{ kg}$$

The number of significant figures in 0.45359237 and 0.4536 is different. Rules for determining the correct number of significant figures to use when reporting a measurement or calculation are given in the following section.

B. Determining the Number of Significant Figures

A reasonably reliable measurement contains at least one figure that is known with certainty, plus one estimated figure to the right of the last known figure. In Figure 2(b), for example, a reasonably reliable estimate of the arrow position is 6.6, although the arrow could be at either 6.5 or 6.7. In this case, the ones figure is known with certainty, and the tenths figure is estimated. Therefore, based on Figure 2(b), the number 6.6 contains two significant figures. If we were to report 6.62 as the arrow position for Figure 2(b), the second estimated figure, 2, would not be significant. In a reasonably reliable estimate, only one estimated figure can be included among the significant figures reported.

Similarly, for reported measurements or results, we assume that only the last numeral is estimated. Based on this assumption, it is not hard to determine the number of significant figures in reported values. For example,

1.75 has 3 significant figures

1.754 has 4 significant figures

17.54 has 4 significant figures

The following two rules apply to correctly reported values.

1. All nonzero numerals are counted as significant figures.

2. The position of the decimal point has no effect on the number of significant figures, as long as the number contains no zeros.

For numbers containing zeros, common sense is very useful for determining the number of significant figures. For example, 2.016 clearly contains four significant figures: The zero is in the middle of the number, so it must be included. On the other hand, with small numbers like 0.08206 and large numbers like 135,000, there can be some confusion about whether zeros at the beginning or the end of a number should be counted. The following rules apply to counting zeros as significant figures.

3. Zeros to the left of all nonzero numerals are not significant.

This means that you start counting significant figures at the nonzero numeral farthest to the left in the number, and count to the right. The following examples illustrate this rule:

0.0821 contains 3 significant figures (start counting at the 8 and count to the right)

0.002 has one significant figure (start counting at the 2)

4. Zeros surrounded by nonzero numerals are significant.

The following examples illustrate this rule:

200.59 has 5 significant figures

2.016 has 4 significant figures

0.08206 has 4 significant figures (start counting at the 8)

Note again that the position of the decimal point does not affect the number of significant figures.

5. Zeros to the right of all nonzero numerals, called *trailing zeros*, may or may not be significant.

(a) If a decimal point appears in the number, all trailing zeros to the right of the decimal point are significant. For example:

0.00640 has 3 significant figures (start counting at the 6; the last zero is to the right of all the nonzero digits and to the right of the decimal point; it is therefore significant)

75.0 has 3 significant figures (same reasoning)

1000.0 has 5 significant figures (all zeros are significant, because the last one is to the right of the decimal point)

(b) If trailing zeros are all to the left of the decimal point, then we must know more about the number to determine whether any of these zeros are significant. Sometimes a reasonable guess is necessary. The following examples clarify this rule.

The number 1000 may contain from one to four significant figures. For example, if you lift an object with your hand and guess that it weighs about 1000 g, this is obviously not an exact measurement. In this case, the measurement and the number has only one significant figure, the 1. If you weigh the same object on a balance that determines mass to the nearest 10 g, then you can be reasonably certain of the first three figures in the measurement. In this case, 1000 has 3 significant figures. If you weigh the object on a balance that determines mass to the nearest gram, then all four figures in 1000 are significant.

As another example, the number 135,000 oz probably represents an approximate measurement, so it likely has only 3 significant figures. The zeros probably are there only to show the position of the decimal point. In cases like this, we cannot be sure whether any of the zeros are significant until we know something about the method of the measurement.

If we know the number of significant figures in 135,000 oz, we can indicate this clearly by using exponential notation to report the measurement number. This is because the digit term in exponential notation contains only significant figures. For example, if we know that a measurement of 135,000 oz has only one significant figure, we can show this clearly by expressing the number as 1×10^5 oz. If a much more exact measurement is made so that 135,000 oz has four significant figures, then we can express the measurement as 1.350×10^5. Thus, an important use of exponential notation is to clearly indicate the number of significant figures in a reported measurement.

C. Rounding Off Numbers

The next few sections explain how significant figures are used in calculations. The general rule about rounding is that **a calculated result can only be as reliable as the least precisely known measurement in the calculation**. This rule makes it necessary to **round off** some numbers, that is, to drop certain digits.

Conventions for rounding off numbers focus on the digit farthest to the right of those that will be kept, the **retained digit**, and the next digit to the right, the **dropped digit**. Thus, if we round off 1.743 to 1.7, the retained digit is 7, and the dropped digit is 4. The following examples show numbers being rounded off to three significant figures.

1. If the dropped digit is less than 5, the retained digit remains unchanged.

For example:

1.634 rounds off to 1.63 (4 is less than 5, so the 3 remains unchanged)

1.6729 rounds off to 1.67 (2 is less than 5, so the 7 remains unchanged)

2. If the dropped digit is a 5 followed by zeros or no digits, the retained digit remains unchanged if it is an even number and is increased by one if it is odd.

For example:

1.635 rounds off to 1.64 (5 with no following digits is dropped, 3 is odd, so the 3 is increased by 1 to 4)

1.625 rounds off to 1.62 (5 with no following digits is dropped, 2 is even, so the 2 remains unchanged)

1.07500 rounds off to 1.08 (5 followed by zeros is dropped, 7 is odd, so the 7 is increased to 8)

3. If the dropped digit is greater than 5 or is a 5 followed by nonzero digits, the retained digit is increased by 1.

For example:

1.637 rounds off to 1.64 (7 is greater than 5, so 3 is increased to 4)

1.647 rounds off to 1.65 (7 is greater than 5, so 4 is increased to 5)

1.48533 rounds off to 1.49 (5 is followed by nonzero digits, so 8 is increased to 9)

D. Rounding Off Calculated Results

In Part C, we noted that a calculated result is only as reliable as the least precisely known measurement in the calculation. We use this rule to determine how many digits to drop when rounding off a calculated result. The type of calculation determines how the rule is applied.

1. Rounding Off in Addition and Subtraction

In addition and subtraction, the least precisely known factor will be the one with the smallest number of decimal places. Therefore, the calculated result must have no more decimal places than the least precisely known number being added or subtracted.

For example, suppose a solution contains 99.6 g of A, 31.62 g of B, and 9.765 g of C. What should be reported as the total mass of the solution? We solve this problem as follows:

mass of A:	99.6 g	®	99.6 g
mass of B:	31.62 g	®	31.6 g
mass of C:	9.765 g	®	9.8 g
total mass:			141.0 g

In other words, we round off all factors until there are no blank spaces in the right-hand column. When using a calculator to do the above addition, we either round off before adding (which requires fewer keystrokes) or we round off the result. In this case, if we use a calculator to add the original numbers, the result is 140.985. We then round off this number to 141.0, which matches the result we obtain when we round off the numbers before adding.

Rounding off in subtraction is done in the same way as in addition. For example, suppose that a beaker containing a solution weighs 72.654 g, while the empty beaker has a mass of 59.6 g. What is the mass of the solution?

mass of beaker and solution:	72.654 g ® 72.7 g
mass of beaker:	59.6 g ® 59.6 g
mass of solution:	13.1 g

Again, if we use a calculator, we must either round off the result or round off the factors first, as shown.

2. Rounding Off in Multiplication and Division

In multiplication and division, the result can be no more reliable than the least precisely known factor. The least precisely known factor in a multiplication or division problem calculation is simply the factor with the fewest significant figures, regardless of the position of the decimal point. The calculated result must be rounded off so that it contains no more significant figures than does the least precisely known factor.

For example, if we use a calculator to multiply 3.142 times 2.2 we get 6.9124. However, we should not report 6.9124 as our result, because the factor 2.2 contains only two significant figures. Therefore, the reported result can have only two significant figures, so 6.9124 must be rounded off to 6.9.

We can do some rounding off before multiplying or dividing. This will decrease the number of keystrokes needed. First, find the factor with the fewest significant figures. Round off all other factors so they have *one more* significant figure than the least precise factor. The calculated result will be the same as if you used the original factors and then rounded off the result at the end.

For example, consider the density calculation discussed at the beginning of this part of the Procedure:

$$d = \frac{14.3216 \text{ g}}{2.00 \text{ mL}} \begin{matrix} \longleftarrow \text{(6 significant figures)} \\ \longleftarrow \text{(3 significant figures)} \end{matrix}$$

Using a calculator, we get the result 7.1608 g/mL, which must be rounded off to 7.16 g/mL (3 significant figures). The reported results, 7.16 g/mL, has the same number of significant figures as does the least precisely known factor, 2.00 mL.

To save keystrokes, we can round off the factors before dividing. In this case, we can round off 14.3216 g

to four significant figures (14.32 g), *one more than* the three significant figures in 2.00 mL. Then we can divide as follows:

$$\frac{14.32 \text{ g}}{2.00 \text{ mL}} = 7.16 \text{ g} / \text{mL}$$

Both methods yield the same result.

E.   Significant Figures in Logarithms

Several areas of chemistry use logarithms, which have two parts, the characteristic and the mantissa. The characteristic consists of the digits to the left of the decimal point. The mantissa consists of the digits to the right of the decimal point. For example, log 2578 = 3.4113. In the logarithm 3.4113, the characteristic is 3 and the mantissa is 4113.

One basic rule governs the number of significant figures that should be reported in a logarithm: the mantissa of a logarithm should have the same number of significant figures as does the original number. Some examples are:

log 2 = 0.3 (1 significant figure in 2)

log 2.0 = 0.30 (2 significant figures in 2.0)

log 2.00 = 0.301 (3 significant figures in 2.00)

$\log 2.0 \times 10^4 = 4.30$ (2 significant figures in 2.0)

$\log 2.00 \times 10^{-5} = -4.699$ (3 significant figures in 2.00)

The rule also applies when determining antilogs. Some examples:

antilog 0.48 = 3.0 (2 significant figures in the mantissa)

antilog 0.477 = 3.00 (3 significant figures in the mantissa)

antilog 3.4771 = 3.000×10^3 (4 significant figures in the mantissa)

Problem Set 2

(Use the spaces provided for the answers and additional paper if necessary.)

1. How many significant figures are contained in each of the following numbers?

   (a) 0.9463   _____

   (b) 0.08206   _____

   (c) 6.0225 ´ 10^{23} _____

   (d) 1.0 ´ 10^{-12} _____

   (e) 1010   _____

2. Round off each of the following numbers to four significant figures.

   (a) 273.15   _____

   (b) 12.652   _____

   (c) 19.9743   _____

   (d) 4.32156   _____

   (e) 0.019807   _____

3. Complete the following calculations, and express each result using the proper number of significant figures.

   (a) $4.196 + 0.0725 + 14.3 =$

   (b) $74.321 - 4.2 =$

   (c) $(8.2156 ´ 10^2) ´ (3.12) =$

   (d) $\dfrac{6.042}{7} =$

   (e) $\dfrac{0.98 ´ 0.230}{0.08206 ´ 298} =$

_____   _____   _____

Dimensional Analysis

prepared by **S. Kay Gunter**, Scottsdale, Arizona,
and **James P. Birk**, Arizona State University

Purpose of the Experiment

Practice using dimensional analysis to solve general chemistry problems using clues such as units or dimensions associated with measurements.

Background Information

How Do You Solve a Problem?

Beginning students in chemistry often see problem-solving as their greatest challenge. Many students believe that solving chemistry problems involves memorizing endless mathematical equations and formulas, a different one for every situation. Relax! Just as there are techniques you can practice to improve your golf game, guitar playing, or cooking, there are techniques that will improve your chemistry problem-solving skills.

One of the most helpful techniques for solving problems is **dimensional analysis**. "Dimensional" refers to the dimensions, or units, associated with the numbers in the problem, such as 60 *seconds/minute* or 120 *grams/liter*. Dimensional analysis is based on the principle that the units in an equation can be treated like the numbers. In other words, in dimensional analysis, we perform the same mathematical operations on the units as we do on the associated numbers—division, multiplication, and especially cancellation.

To demonstrate how dimensional analysis works, let's analyze a problem we can solve almost without thinking. We'll break the problem-solving process into steps, write out the steps, and then apply the steps to solve more complicated everyday problems, as well as chemistry problems.

Here's the problem: Express 90 minutes in hours. For most of us, the answer comes automatically: 90 minutes is an hour and a half. Let's analyze the unconscious process we use to arrive at that answer. It takes a lot longer to explain it than to do it!

First, we decide what the problem asks us to find or calculate. In this case, it's straightforward: We need to find the number of hours (hr) that corresponds to 90 minutes (min).

To solve this problem, we have to know how many minutes there are in one hour. We can express this relationship as an **equivalence statement**: 1 hr = 60 min. From this equivalence statement, we can construct a **conversion factor** to change minutes into hours. To do so, we divide each side of the equivalence statement by 60 min:

$$\frac{1 \text{ hr}}{60 \text{ min}} = \frac{\cancel{60 \text{ min}}}{\cancel{60 \text{ min}}} = 1$$

Because we are dividing both sides by the same quantity, we know that the two sides of the resulting equation are also equal. Notice that the conversion factor, 1 hr/60 min, is equal to 1, an equivalence often called unity . This is true of all conversion factors, because the numerator and denominator always contain equivalent quantities. Because all conversion factors equal 1, we can multiply any measurement by a conversion factor without changing the total value of the measurement. All we are doing is changing the units used to express the measurement.

Next, we multiply the original quantity, 90 minutes, by the conversion factor to obtain the desired equivalent quantity expressed in hours:

$$90 \text{ min} \left(\frac{1\,\text{hr}}{60\,\text{min}}\right) = \frac{(90\,\cancel{\text{min}})(1\,\text{hr})}{60\,\cancel{\text{min}}} = 1.5 \text{ hr}$$

Notice that the original unit, minutes, cancels, and the resulting quantity is expressed in the desired unit, hours.

Finally, we check the answer for reasonableness. We know that 90 min is longer than 1 hr, but not as long as 2 hr, so 1.5 hr is a reasonable answer.

To further study our reasonableness check, let's more closely examine our choice of conversion factor. For example, we can obtain another conversion factor from our original equivalence statement, 1 hr = 60 min, by dividing each side by 1 hr instead of 60 min.

$$\frac{1\,\text{hr}}{1\,\text{hr}} = \frac{60\,\text{min}}{1\,\text{hr}} = 1$$

This conversion factor is also equal to unity. However, look what happens when we multiply our original quantity, 90 min, by this conversion factor:

$$90 \text{ min} \left(\frac{60\,\text{min}}{1\,\text{hr}}\right) = \frac{(90\,\text{min})(60\,\text{min})}{1\,\text{hr}}$$
$$= 5400 \frac{\text{min}^2}{\text{hr}}$$

There are two clear reasons why this answer is unreasonable: (1) the units (min²/hr) are definitely not the ones we want (hr); and (2) we know that 90 min isn't more than 5000 hr. Thus, we can conclude that 60 min/hr is the wrong conversion factor to use in solving this problem.

Every equivalence statement provides two such inverse conversion factors. The correct conversion factor to use depends on how the problem is expressed. In every case, when we use the correct conversion factor, the units we want to eliminate cancel, leaving only the units we want the answer expressed in. Using the incorrect conversion factor will give an unreasonable answer, expressed in nonsensical units. This should be a clear warning that we used an upside-down or otherwise incorrect conversion factor.

The preceding example illustrates the most compelling reason for using dimensional analysis to solve problems: it keeps us from multiplying when we should divide, or dividing when we should multiply. If the units in our answer are the desired ones, odds are good that we solved the problem correctly, barring arithmetic errors. If the units in our answer are not the desired ones, we probably used the wrong conversion factor. In problem solving, choosing incorrect conversion factors is more common than making arithmetic mistakes.

Now that we've analyzed a technique for solving an everyday problem, let's write out the steps and expand them, so the technique can be used to solve other types of problems, including chemistry examples:

Step 1.   Decide what the problem is asking you to do. Begin by reading the problem carefully. If the definitions of any terms are unclear, look them up. If an equation is given to use, be sure that you understand the meaning of any symbols or variables involved. Look for clues in the statement of the problem, words such as "calculate," "determine," "how much," "what mass," or "what volume." Once you understand what the problem is asking you to do, write down the units you will need for the answer.

Step 2.   Determine the relationships between the information given in the problem and the desired answer.   In our original example, we recognized that the relationship between the data given, "90 minutes," and the desired answer, "hours," could be expressed by the equivalence statement 1 hr = 60 min. This relationship was not stated in the original problem. We had to remember the relationship (or look it up), in order to apply it to this problem. When solving problems, you will often find that memory will serve as the source of these relationships. At other times you may need to refer to a previous paragraph, table, or figure in your textbook, a laboratory manual, or a data handbook.

As a word of caution, sometimes a problem contains more information than you need to solve it. Therefore, you should not assume that you must use a particular unit in your problem-solving calculations, just because the unit is included in the description of the problem. Critically examine all data and reject any data that aren't pertinent to the desired answer.

The equivalence statements must be valid. If we base our solution on an incorrect equivalence statement, such as 16 in. = 1 ft, or an unbalanced chemical equation, even dimensional analysis cannot help us to obtain the correct answer. However, as long as all the equivalence statements and equations we use are valid, dimensional analysis should keep us from making errors in either algebra or logic.

In our original example, the relationship between the two units could be expressed simply, as 1 hr = 60 min. However, the relationship is often more complex, requiring a series of related equivalence statements and their derived conversion factors. In other cases, a description of the relationship requires the use of an empirical or theoretical equation, or the application of a chemical principle. The section entitled "Applying Dimensional Analysis to General Chemistry Problems" on the next page presents examples of these and other problems.

Step 3.   Set up the problem by writing a logical, concise equation for solving the problem, based on the relationships determined in Step 2. Derive the conversion factors needed to achieve the desired answer. Be sure that the units you need to eliminate cancel, leaving only the desired units in the answer.

When a series of related conversion factors is required, map out the correct sequence to follow. For example, suppose that the solution to a problem involves the number of centimeters in one mile, but you can't find a table containing this information. However, you probably know (or can easily look up) the number of feet in one mile, the number of inches in one foot, and the number of centimeters in one inch. In this case, the correct sequence of units is:

$$mi \rightarrow ft \rightarrow in. \rightarrow cm$$

The equation needed to solve this problem should start with the quantity given, 1 mile, and then follow the above sequence, as shown in Equation 1.

$$1\,mi \left(\frac{5280\,ft}{1\,mi}\right)\left(\frac{12\,in.}{1\,ft}\right)\left(\frac{2.54\,cm}{1\,in.}\right) = 1.61 \times 10^5 \, cm$$

(Eq. 1)

Step 4.   Check your answer to make sure it is reasonable in terms of both magnitude and units. This step is just as important as the preceding three. For example, suppose we are asked to calculate the daily volume of liquid antacid an ulcer patient must consume to neutralize his excess stomach acid. We calculate 24 L as the answer. Remembering that a liter and a quart are about the same volume, we realize that 24 L is an incredible amount of liquid for one person to drink daily. However, because liter is an acceptable volume unit for the answer, the conversion factors we used are probably correct. Therefore, we probably made an arithmetic error or omitted the metric prefix, milli- (10^{-3}), somewhere. Clearly, we need to recheck our calculations and, possibly, the equation we used for finding the answer, in order to find the error. If our answer had instead been 24 mol, we would know to check the conversion factors, because mole is not a volume unit.

When dealing with unfamiliar units or relationships, you may not always know whether or not an answer is reasonable. In such cases, just check your arithmetic.

Solving Sample Problems in Detail

We will work two problems in detail, analyzing the solutions step by step.

Example 1:   Dimensional analysis may be applied to a relatively complicated non-chemical problem.

Problem: Calculate how many gallons of water are required to fill a residential fish pond, measuring 8.0 ft by 6.0 ft by 1.5 ft.

Step 1.   The problem clearly states the physical dimensions involved and units desired in the answer: volume of water in gallons.

Step 2.   The problem data are given in units of length (feet), but the answer must be in units of volume (gallons). Thus, we recognize that the first step is to calculate the volume of the pool:

volume, $ft^3 = (l)(w)(h) = (8.0\,ft)(6.0\,ft)(1.5\,ft) = 72\,ft^3$

Next, we need to know the relationship between cubic feet and gallons. A handbook tells us that 1 $ft^3 = 7.481$ gal (U.S.). Thus, the conversion is a simple one, described by the following equation.

$$72\,ft^3 \left(\frac{7.481\,gal}{1\,ft^3}\right) = 540 \, gal$$

Step 3.   If a data handbook is not available, we can solve this problem using the following simple equivalence statements that we either already know or can look up in a textbook:

1 ft = 12 in.	1 in. = 2.54 cm	10^3 cm^3 = 1 L
1 L = 1.06 qt	4 qt = 1 gal	

Our route for using the simple equivalency statements is:

$$ft^3 \rightarrow in.^3 \rightarrow cm^3 \rightarrow L \rightarrow qt \rightarrow gal$$

The correct equation is shown in Equation 2. Notice that if we raise to some power one of the units in a problem-solving equation (ft^3, for example), we must also raise to the same power all terms that contain that unit in the conversion factors. That's why the cm/in. factor is shown cubed. Otherwise, the units will not cancel. Also, notice that the answer is the same, when using the proper number of significant figures (two), regardless of the order of the conversion factors.

volume, gal =

$$72\,\cancel{ft^3}\left(\frac{12\,\cancel{in.}}{1\,\cancel{ft}}\right)^3\left(\frac{2.54\,\cancel{cm}}{1\,\cancel{in.}}\right)^3\left(\frac{1\,\cancel{L}}{10^3\,\cancel{cm^3}}\right)\left(\frac{1.06\,\cancel{qt}}{1\,\cancel{L}}\right)\left(\frac{1\,gal}{4\,\cancel{qt}}\right)$$

$$= \frac{(72)(12)^3\,(2.54)^3\,(1)(1.06)(1\,gal)}{(1)^3\,(1)^3\,(10^3)(1)(4)} = 540\ gal$$

(Eq. 2)

Step 4.   Because the units that cancel leave us with the units we want in our answer, we can feel confident that we used the correct conversion factors. If you don't know whether or not 540 gal is a reasonable estimate of the amount of water needed to fill a pond this size, check the arithmetic.

Example 2:   Dimensional analysis can also be used within an equation.

Problem: Calculate the wavelength, in meters, of the radio waves broadcast from station KZON-FM, Phoenix, Arizona, operating at 101.5 MHz.

Step 1.   The physical quantity and units desired are clearly stated: wavelength in meters.

Step 2.   Hz is the symbol for hertz, a unit of frequency ($1\ Hz = 1\ s^{-1}$). Frequency and wavelength are related by the equation $\lambda\nu = c$, where λ = wavelength, ν = frequency, and c = the speed of light in a vacuum, $3.00 \times 10^{10}\ cm\ s^{-1}$.

Step 3.   The relationship $\lambda\nu = c$ may be rearranged to isolate wavelength: $\lambda = c/\nu$. Substituting the actual values for c and ν, we obtain:

$$\lambda = \frac{3.00 \times 10^{10}\ cm\ s^{-1}}{101.5\ MHz}$$

However, with the equation in this form, no units cancel. If we tried to use the equation to calculate λ, the answer would not be in meters. Instead, we must make some unit conversions within the equation.

Knowing that $1\ MHz = 10^6\ Hz$ and $1\ m = 100\ cm$, we can convert MHz $\rightarrow s^{-1}$ and cm $\rightarrow$ m. Then the units will cancel properly, leaving only meters in the answer:

$$\lambda,\,m = \left(\frac{3.00 \times 10^{10}\ \cancel{cm}\ \cancel{s^{-1}}}{101.5\,\cancel{MHz}}\right)\left(\frac{1\,\cancel{MHz}}{10^6\,\cancel{Hz}}\right)\left(\frac{1\,\cancel{Hz}}{1\,\cancel{s^{-1}}}\right)\left(\frac{1\,m}{100\,\cancel{cm}}\right)$$
$$= 2.96\ m$$

Step 4.   Because the units cancel properly, we can assume that the conversion factors are correct. Radio waves are among the longest electromagnetic waves, so this is not an unreasonable answer.

Applying Dimensional Analysis to General Chemistry Problems

The following examples illustrate the use of dimensional analysis in solving general chemistry problems. Solving these problems will sharpen your problem-solving skills. Some problems use units that may not be familiar to you. Use dimensional analysis to solve these problems, even if you don't fully understand the meaning of the units involved. The meanings of such units and the bases for the equivalencies among them will become clearer to you as you proceed further in your study of chemistry.

In each of the following examples, Steps 1 and 4, deciding what the problem is asking for and checking the answer for reasonableness, respectively, are not written out. We only show Steps 2 and 3, which involve equivalence statements, sequences, and conversion factors. Use the metric prefixes and common equivalence statements in Tables 1 and 2 to solve these sample problems.

I.   Simple Unit Conversions and Ratios of Units

Example 1:   International soccer games are generally played on a field 115 yd long. Convert this distance to meters.

Answer 1:   From Table 2, we know that 1 yd = 0.9144 m, so the conversion equation is:

$$distance,\,m = 115\,\cancel{yd}\left(\frac{0.9144\ m}{1\,\cancel{yd}}\right) = 105\ m$$

Answer 2:   If a table of equivalence statements were not available, you could calculate the distance

Table 1 *Metric prefixes*

power of 10	prefix	symbol
−18	atto-	a
−15	femto-	f
−12	pico-	p
−9	nano-	n
−6	micro-	μ
−3	milli-	m
−2	centi-	c
−1	deci-	d
+18	exa-	E
+15	peta-	P
+12	tera-	T
+9	giga-	G
+6	mega-	M
+3	kilo-	k
+2	hecto-	h
+1	deka-	da

Table 2 *Common equivalence statements*

mass:	1 lb = 0.4536 kg
	16 oz = 1 lb
	1 ton = 2000 lb
	1 amu = 1.6606×10^{-24} g
length:	1 in. = 2.54×10^{-2} m = 2.54 cm
	1 Å = 10^{-10} m = 10^{-8} cm
	1 ft = 12 in. = 0.3048 m
	1 yd = 3 ft = 36 in. = 0.9144 m
	1 mi = 1760 yd = 5280 ft
	= 1609 m
volume:	1 L = 10^{-3} m^3 = 1 dm^3 = 10^3 cm^3
	1 L = 1.06 qt
	1 gal = 4 qt = 8 pt = 3.785 L
	1 pt = 2 cups
	= 16 fluid ounces (fl oz)
time:	1 min = 60 s
	1 hr = 60 min = 3600 s
	1 d = 24 hr = 1440 min
	= 86,400 s
temperature:	°C = K − 273.15
	°C = 5/9(°F − 32)
force:	1 dyn = 10^{-5} N
pressure:	1 bar = 10^5 N/m^2 = 10^5 Pa
	1 torr = 1 mm Hg = 133.322 Pa
	1 atm = 760 torr = 101,325 N/m^2
	= 101,325 Pa
energy:	1 cal = 4.184 J
	1 erg = 10^{-7} J
	1 eV = 1.6022×10^{-19} J

using common equivalence statements that you probably already know, following the route: yd → in. → cm → m

$$\text{distance, m} = 115 \text{ yd} \left(\frac{36 \text{ in.}}{1 \text{ yd}}\right)\left(\frac{2.54 \text{ cm}}{1 \text{ in.}}\right)\left(\frac{1 \text{ m}}{100 \text{ cm}}\right)$$
$$= 105 \text{ m}$$

Example 2: In our body-conscious culture, there's a lot of talk about the "calories" in various kinds of food. Few people remember that the original term was "Calorie," with a capital C, which actually means kilocalories (kcal).

To maintain their weight, moderately active people need to eat about 13,000 calories daily, or 13 Calories (kcal), per pound (lb) of body weight. Convert this amount of energy to kilojoules (kJ), another unit of energy.

Answer: Using Table 2, we find that a direct conversion is possible.

$$\text{energy, kJ} = 13,000 \text{ cal}\left(\frac{4.184 \text{ J}}{1 \text{ cal}}\right)\left(\frac{1 \text{ kJ}}{10^3 \text{ J}}\right) = 54 \text{ kJ}$$

Example 3: Calculate the total weight in pounds of a runner if his body weighs 158.0 lb, his clothes weigh 8.0 oz, and his shoes weigh 10.0 oz.

Answer: To add or subtract measurements, all units involved must be identical.

$$\text{mass}_{total} = \text{mass}_{runner} + \text{mass}_{clothes} + \text{mass}_{shoes}$$

Based on Table 2, we can write either

$$\text{mass, oz} = 158.0 \text{ lb}\left(\frac{16 \text{ oz}}{1 \text{ lb}}\right) + 8.0 \text{ oz} + 10.0 \text{ oz}$$
$$= 2546 \text{ oz}$$

or

$$\text{mass, lb} = 158.0 \text{ lb} + (8.0 \text{ oz} + 10.0 \text{ oz})\left(\frac{1 \text{ lb}}{16 \text{ oz}}\right)$$
$$= 159.1 \text{ lb}$$

Example 4: Light in a vacuum travels at 3.00×10^{10} cm s^{-1}. Mars is an average of 141 million mi from Earth, and it travels in its orbit at 15 mi s^{-1}. How many hours would it take for a laser beam from the Earth to reach Mars?

Note: Two speeds are given in this problem, but only the speed at which light travels in a vacuum is relevant.

From Table 2 we know that 1 mi = 1.609×10^3 m.

Answer: time = distance/speed

$$\text{time, hr} = \left(\frac{1.41\times10^8 \, \text{mi}}{3.00\times10^{10} \, \text{cm s}^{-1}}\right)\left(\frac{1.609\times10^3 \, \text{m}}{1 \, \text{mi}}\right)$$

$$\left(\frac{10^2 \, \text{cm}}{1 \, \text{m}}\right)\left(\frac{1 \, \text{hr}}{60 \, \text{min}}\right)\left(\frac{1 \, \text{min}}{60 \, \text{s}}\right) = .21 \, \text{hr}$$

Note: Using Tables 1 and 2, and the four basic steps for solving problems using dimensional analysis, solve the problems in Problem Set 1. Write your answers on a separate sheet of paper.

Problem Set 1

1.1 On average, the moon takes 27 d, 7 hr, and 43.2 min to make a complete circuit around the Earth. Express this time in hours.

1.2 David Robinson, a professional basketball player, is 7 ft, 1.0 in. tall. Convert his height to centimeters.

1.3 A sheet of standard U.S. typing paper measures 8.50 in. × 11.0 in. What is its area in cm^2?

1.4 One of the oldest elephants on record lived for 130 yr. How many minutes is that? (Use 1 yr = 365 d)

1.5 How many gallons of soft drink are there in a 2.0-L bottle?

1.6 What mass of cereal in kilograms is in a 40.0-oz box?

1.7 A diamond is made of pure carbon. The distance between any two neighboring carbon atoms in a diamond is 1.54 angstroms (Å). What is this distance in inches?

1.8 If an audiotape playing at a speed of 1.875 in. s^{-1} takes 45.0 min to play through one side, what is the length of the tape in feet? in meters?

1.9 The speed limit on many Australian highways is 100 km hr^{-1}. Convert this to mi hr^{-1} (round to the nearest whole number).

1.10 What is the volume in mL of 1.00 pt of heavy cream?

1.11 The average density of whole milk is 1.034 g cm^{-3}. What is its density in lb gal^{-1}?

1.12 It is 2374 mi between Phoenix, Arizona, and Philadelphia, Pennsylvania. What is this distance in km?

1.13 The legendary racehorse Secretariat won the 1973 Kentucky Derby with a time of 1 min, 59.4 s. The course is 1.25 mi long. Calculate the horse's average speed in mi hr^{-1}.

1.14 The density of water at room temperature (25 °C) is 0.9970 g cm^{-3}. How many pounds does the water in a full 5.00-gal pail weigh?

1.15 If the barometric pressure on a mountain top in Colorado is 521 mm of mercury, what is the pressure in inches of Hg? in atmospheres? in Pascals?

1.16 If an oxygen molecule is moving at 4.78×10^4 cm s^{-1}, what is its speed in mi hr^{-1}?

1.17 Nutrition experts recommend that you drink at least 8 cups of water daily. If your local water supply contains 1.00 part fluoride (by mass) per million parts water, how many milligrams of fluoride would you consume daily in your 8 cups of water? (Use 1.00 g cm^{-3} as the density of water.)

1.18 Light in a vacuum travels at a speed of 3.00×10^8 m s^{-1}. Pluto's average distance from the Sun is 3.6 billion miles. How many minutes does it take sunlight to reach Pluto?

1.19 The temperature of an oxyacetylene torch flame can reach as high as 3137 °C. What is this temperature in °F?

1.20 If the gasoline in a full 20.0-gallon tank weighs 116 lb, what is the density of gasoline in g mL^{-1}?

1.21 Dry sand has a density of 1.5 g cm^{-3}. A child's sandbox, measuring 4.0 ft by 5.0 ft, is filled with sand to a depth of 6.0 in. What is the mass of the sand in kg? in lb?

1.22 The hottest temperature yet recorded in Phoenix, Arizona, was 122 °F on June 26, 1990. What is that temperature in °C? in K?

II. Conversions among Masses, Moles, and Numbers of Particles

The relationships among mass, number of moles, and number of particles is shown by the following routes:

$$\text{mass} \xleftrightarrow{\text{AM, MM, or FM}} \begin{array}{c} \text{number} \\ \text{of moles} \end{array} \xleftrightarrow{\text{N}} \begin{array}{c} \text{number of atoms,} \\ \text{molecules, ions} \\ \text{or formula units} \end{array}$$

The double-headed arrows indicate that we can travel this route in either direction. We can also start at any point and travel only a portion of the entire route.

The symbols above the arrows indicate the data involved in the equivalence statements needed for making each conversion: atomic mass (AM), molar mass (MM), formula mass (FM), and Avogadro's number (N). These equivalence statements are determined as follows:

(a) 1 mol = amount of matter in 1 AM of **atoms:** 1 mol C = 12.01 g C

(b) 1 mol = amount of matter in 1 MM of **molecules**: 1 mol CO_2 = 44.01 g CO_2

(c) 1 mol = amount of matter in 1 FM of **formula units or ions**: 1 mol NaCl = 58.44 g NaCl; 1 mol SO_4^{2-} = 96.06 g SO_4^{2-}

(d) 1 mol = N = 6.022×10^{23} atoms, molecules, formula units, or ions: 1 mol CO_2 = 6.022×10^{23} CO_2 molecules; 1 mol NO_3^- = 6.022×10^{20} NO_3 ions

Example 1: How many moles of NaCl are in 75.0 g of NaCl?

Answer: mass of NaCl $\xrightarrow{\text{FM}}$ number of moles of NaCl

FM: 1 mol NaCl = 58.44 g NaCl

$$\begin{array}{l} \text{number} \\ \text{moles of} \\ \text{NaCl, mol} \end{array} = 75.0 \text{ g NaCl} \left(\frac{1 \text{ mol NaCl}}{58.44 \text{ g NaCl}} \right)$$
$$= 1.28 \text{ mol NaCl}$$

Example 2: How many molecules of CO_2 are in 25.0 g CO_2?

Answer:

$$\text{mass} \xleftrightarrow{\text{MM}} \begin{array}{c} \text{number} \\ \text{of moles} \end{array} \xleftrightarrow{\text{N}} \begin{array}{c} \text{number} \\ \text{of molecules} \end{array}$$

MM: 1 mol CO_2 = 44.01 g CO_2

$$\begin{array}{l} \text{number of} \\ \text{molecules of } CO_2 \end{array} = 25.0 \text{ g } CO_2 \left(\frac{1 \text{ mol } CO_2}{44.01 \text{ g } CO_2} \right)$$
$$\left(\frac{6.022 \times 10^{23} \text{ molecules } CO_2}{1 \text{ mol } CO_2} \right)$$
$$= 3.42 \times 10^{23} \text{ molecules } CO_2$$

Problem Set 2

2.1 Find the number of moles in 100.0 g of each of the following:
(a) O_3 (ozone)   (b) H_2SO_4 (sulfuric acid)
(c) $Ca_3(PO_4)_2$ (d) $C_{12}H_{22}O_{11}$ (table sugar)
(e) Au (gold)

2.2 Find the mass of 0.67 mol of each of the following:
(a) Ag (silver)   (b) C_4H_{10} (butane)
(c) SiO_2 (quartz) (d) N_2O (laughing gas)
(e) $Mg(OH)_2$ (stomach antacid)

2.3 Find the number of particles in 100.0 g of each of the following:
(a) O^{2-} (b) O_2 (c) MgO
(d) $C_8H_{10}N_4O_2$ (caffeine)
(e) $Fe_3Al_2(SiO_4)_3$ (garnet)

2.4 Find the mass of 2.00×10^{23} particles of each of the following:
(a) NH_3 (b) Na_2CrO_4
(c) $C_6H_{11}OBr$ (tear gas)
(d) $C_{10}H_{14}NO_5PS$ (parathion, an insecticide)
(e) $NH_2C_6H_4CO_2H$ (PABA, *para*-aminobenzoic acid)

III. Percent Composition and Chemical Formulas

The relationships connecting percent composition and chemical formulas are shown in the following route using a hypothetical compound composed of substances *A* and *B*.

$$\text{mass} \atop \% A \xleftarrow{\text{100-g sample}} \text{mass} \atop \text{of } A \xleftarrow{\text{AM}} \text{number of} \atop \text{moles of } A$$

$$\uparrow$$

$$\text{subscripts} \atop \text{in formula} \longleftrightarrow \text{empirical} \atop \text{formula} \xrightarrow{\text{MM and FM}} \text{molecular} \atop \text{formula}$$

$$\downarrow$$

$$\text{mass} \atop \% B \xleftarrow{\text{100-g sample}} \text{mass} \atop \text{of } B \xleftarrow{\text{AM}} \text{number of} \atop \text{moles of } B$$

The atomic mass (AM), molar mass (MM), and formula mass (FM) of substances involved are the sources of the conversion factors necessary for the indicated steps. In addition, the subscripts in a chemical formula provide us with another conversion factor. For example, given the general formula A_xB_y, we can write the equivalence statement, x mol of $A = y$ mol of B. If the ratio x/y is an integer, we can derive the empirical formula directly: $(AB)_{x/y}$.

The concept of mass percent is used to convert chemical composition data presented in terms of mass percentages to data expressed as masses in grams. Using a 100-g sample as the basis for our calculations eliminates the units we don't want, as illustrated by the following examples.

Example 1: Ethylene is the plant hormone responsible for the ripening of fruit. It is also the starting material for many plastics, such as polyethylene and polystyrene. Ethylene is 85.63% C and 14.37% H, and has a molar mass of 28.05 g mol^{-1}. What are the empirical formula and the molecular formula for ethylene?

Answer: The path is from left to right along the route map shown above.

$$85.63\% \text{ C} = 85.63 \text{ g C}/100 \text{ g ethylene}; \quad 14.37\% \text{ H} = 14.37 \text{ g H}/100 \text{ g ethylene}$$

$$\text{number of} \atop \text{moles of C} = 100 \text{ g ethylene} \left(\frac{85.63 \text{ g C}}{100 \text{ g ethylene}} \right) \left(\frac{1 \text{ mol C}}{12.01 \text{ g C}} \right) = 7.13 \text{ mol C}$$

$$\text{number of} \atop \text{moles of H} = 100 \text{ g ethylene} \left(\frac{14.37 \text{ g H}}{100 \text{ g ethylene}} \right) \left(\frac{1 \text{ mol H}}{1.008 \text{ g H}} \right) = 14.26 \text{ mol H}$$

Number of moles of H/number of moles of C = $14.26 \text{ mol}_H / 7.13 \text{ mol}_C = 2.00 \text{ mol}_H / \text{mol}_C$. This yields the empirical formula, CH_2.

$$\text{molar mass} = 12.01 \text{ g mol}^{-1} + (2 \times 1.008 \text{ g mol}^{-1}) = 14.03 \text{ g mol}^{-1}$$

$$\text{molecular} \atop \text{formula} = \text{empirical} \atop \text{formula} \left(\frac{1 \text{ mol CH}_2}{14.03 \text{ g}} \right) \left(\frac{28.06 \text{ g}}{1 \text{ mol molecules}} \right) = CH_2 \frac{2 \text{ mol CH}_2}{1 \text{ mol molecules}} = (CH_2)_2 = C_2H_4$$

Example 2: Determine the percent composition of ethylene glycol, $C_2H_6O_2$, a common component of antifreeze. MM of $C_2H_6O_2$ is 62.07 g mol^{-1}.

Answer: The path is from right to left along the route map.

$$\% \text{C} = \left(\frac{2 \text{ mol C}}{1 \text{ mol glycol}} \right) \left(\frac{12.01 \text{ g C}}{1 \text{ mol C}} \right) \left(\frac{1 \text{ mol glycol}}{62.07 \text{ g glycol}} \right) (100\%) = 38.70\%$$

$$\% H = \left(\frac{6\,\text{mol H}}{1\,\text{mol glycol}} \right) \left(\frac{1.008\,\text{g H}}{1\,\text{mol H}} \right) \left(\frac{1\,\text{mol glycol}}{62.07\,\text{g glycol}} \right) (100\%) = 9.74\%$$

$$\% O = \left(\frac{2\,\text{mol O}}{1\,\text{mol glycol}} \right) \left(\frac{16.00\,\text{g O}}{1\,\text{mol O}} \right) \left(\frac{1\,\text{mol glycol}}{62.07\,\text{g glycol}} \right) (100\%) = 51.55\%$$

Example 3: The oxidation of 50.0 g of manganese produces 79.1 g of an oxide. Calculate (a) the percent composition and (b) the empirical formula of this oxide.

Answer (a):   mass of $A \rightarrow$ mass% A $\qquad\qquad$ mass of $B \rightarrow$ mass% B

$$\left(\frac{50.0\,\text{g Mn}}{79.1\,\text{g oxide}} \right) (100\%) = 63.2\%\,\text{Mn}; \qquad \left(\frac{29.1\,\text{g O}}{79.1\,\text{g oxide}} \right) (100\%) = 36.8\%\,\text{O}$$

Answer (b):   mass of $A \rightarrow$ number of moles of A

$$\uparrow$$
subscripts in formula
$$\downarrow$$

mass of $B \rightarrow$ number of moles of B

$$\text{number of moles of Mn} = 50.0\,\text{g Mn} \left(\frac{1\,\text{mol Mn}}{54.94\,\text{g Mn}} \right) = 0.91\,\text{mol Mn}$$

$$\text{number of moles of O} = 29.1\,\text{g O} \left(\frac{1\,\text{mol O}}{16.00\,\text{g O}} \right) = 1.82\,\text{mol O}$$

Then, we can calculate number of moles of O/number of moles of Mn = 1.82 mol$_O$/0.91 mol$_{Mn}$ = 2.00 mol$_O$/mol$_{Mn}$. This yields the empirical formula, MnO_2.

Example 4: Oxidation of 10.0 g of aluminum produces 18.9 g of an aluminum oxide. Calculate (a) the percent composition and (b) the empirical formula of this oxide.

Answer (a):   mass of $A \rightarrow$ mass% A $\qquad\qquad$ mass of $B \rightarrow$ mass% B

$$\left(\frac{10.0\,\text{g Al}}{18.9\,\text{g oxide}} \right) (100\%) = 52.9\%\,\text{Al}; \qquad \left(\frac{8.9\,\text{g O}}{18.9\,\text{g oxide}} \right) (100\%) = 47.1\%\,\text{O}$$

Answer (b):   mass of $A \rightarrow$ number of moles of A

$$\uparrow$$
subscripts in formula
$$\downarrow$$

mass of $B \rightarrow$ number of moles of B

$$\text{number of moles of Al} = 10.0\,\text{g Al} \left(\frac{1\,\text{mol Al}}{27.0\,\text{g Al}} \right) = 0.37\,\text{mol Al}$$

$$\text{number of moles of O} = 8.9\,\text{g O} \left(\frac{1\,\text{mol O}}{16.00\,\text{g O}} \right) = 0.556\,\text{mol O}$$

We can calculate number of moles of O/number of moles of Al = 0.556 mol$_O$/0.370 mol$_{Al}$ = 1.50 mol$_O$/mol$_{Al}$. This yields the empirical formula ($Al_{1.0}O_{1.5}$). But all subscripts must be whole numbers, so we multiply the subscripts in the empirical formula subscripts by 2 to give the correct empirical formula Al_2O_3, ($Al_{1.0}O_{1.5}$)(2).

Problem Set 3

3.1 Determine the empirical and molecular formulas of the following substances:

   (a) hydrogen peroxide; 5.94% H, 94.06% O; MM = 34.01 g mol^{-1}

   (b) disilane; 9.73% H, 90.27% Si; MM = 62.23 g mol^{-1}

   (c) benzoyl peroxide; 69.42% C, 4.16% H, 26.42% O; MM = 242.22 g mol^{-1}

   (d) phosphorus sulfide; 27.87% P, 72.13% S; MM = 444.58 g mol^{-1}

   (e) disulfiram (Antabuse); 40.50% C, 6.80% H, 9.45% N, 43.25% S; MM = 296.54 g mol^{-1}

   (f) alumina; 52.91% Al, 47.08% O; MM = 101.96 g mol^{-1}

3.2 Determine the percent composition of the following compounds:

   (a) BF_3 (b) KCN   (c) $BaSO_4$

   (d) $Ni(CO)_4$ (e) $(NH_4)_2Cr_2O_7$

IV. Reaction Stoichiometry and Balanced Equations

The coefficients in a *balanced* chemical equation can be used to write conversion factors. For example, the general equation, $xA + yB \rightarrow zC$, yields the following equivalence statement:

$$x \text{ mol of } A = y \text{ mol of } B = z \text{ mol of } C$$

The general route for calculating the amounts of materials that react or are produced by the reaction described by this equation is:

$$\text{mass of } A \xleftrightarrow{\text{AM, MM, or FM}} \text{number of moles of } A \xleftrightarrow[\text{in equation}]{\text{coefficients}} \text{number of moles of } B \xleftrightarrow{\text{AM, MM, or FM}} \text{mass of } B$$

Example 1:   Ammonia is prepared by the Haber process, which combines nitrogen and hydrogen gases in a reaction described by the equation:

$$N_2(g) + 3 H_2(g) \rightarrow 2 NH_3(g)$$

What mass of hydrogen is necessary to completely react 50.0 g N_2?

Answer:

$$g\ N_2 \rightarrow \frac{\text{number of}}{\text{moles of } N_2} \rightarrow \frac{\text{number of}}{\text{moles of } H_2} \rightarrow g\ H_2$$

$$\text{mass of } H_2 = 50.0\ g\ N_2 \left(\frac{1\ mol\ N_2}{28.02\ g\ N_2}\right)\left(\frac{3\ mol\ H_2}{1\ mol\ N_2}\right)\left(\frac{2.02\ g\ H_2}{1\ mol\ H_2}\right) = 10.8\ g\ H_2$$

Example 2:   Given 35.0 g N_2 and 35.0 g H_2 reacting according to the equation in Example 1, which material will react completely, and which will be present in excess? How much NH_3 will be formed?

Answer:

$$\text{mass of } H_2 \text{ needed to complete react 35.0 g } N_2 = 35.0\ g\ N_2 \left(\frac{1\ mol\ N_2}{28.02\ g\ N_2}\right)\left(\frac{3\ mol\ H_2}{1\ mol\ N_2}\right)\left(\frac{2.02\ g\ H_2}{1\ mol\ H_2}\right) = 7.57\ g\ H_2$$

Thus, there is an excess of H_2 (35.0 g H_2 available) and N_2 is the limiting reactant. The amount of NH_3 formed is dictated by the amount of N_2, the amount of the limiting reactant.

$$\text{mass of } NH_3 \text{ formed} = 35.0\ g\ N_2 \left(\frac{1\ mol\ N_2}{28.02\ g\ N_2}\right)\left(\frac{2\ mol\ NH_3}{1\ mol\ N_2}\right)\left(\frac{17.03\ g\ NH_3}{1\ mol\ NH_3}\right) = 42.5\ g\ NH_3$$

Problem Set 4

4.1   For each of the following balanced equations, calculate the mass of the second reactant needed to completely react with 100 g of the first reactant.

(a) $2 K(s) + 2 H_2O(g) \rightarrow 2 KOH(aq) + H_2(g)$

(b) $2 Al(s) + 3 F_2(g) \rightarrow 2 AlF_3(s)$

(c) $4 NH_3(g) + 5 O_2(g) \rightarrow 4 NO(g) + 6 H_2O(g)$

(d) $Fe_2O_3(s) + 3 C(s) \rightarrow 2 Fe(l) + 3 CO(g)$

(e) $CaC_2(s) + 2 H_2O(l) \rightarrow Ca(OH)_2(s) + C_2H_2(g)$

(f) $SiO_2(s) + 4 HF(g) \rightarrow SiF_4(g) + 2 H_2O(l)$

(g) $2 C_4H_{10}(g) + 13 O_2(g) \rightarrow$
$$8 CO_2(g) + 10 H_2O(g)$$

(h) $BaCl_2(aq) + Na_2SO_4(aq) \rightarrow$
$$2 NaCl(aq) + BaSO_4(s)$$

4.2   Given 100.0 g of each reactant in the reactions described by the preceding equations, which reactant is the limiting reactant, and what mass of the first product listed will be formed?

V.   Solution Concentrations and Volumes

Solutions are an important part of chemistry, and we need to perform a variety of calculations when dealing with solutions. For example, we may need to calculate the volume of a solution, in order to obtain the number of moles of solute necessary for a reaction. Or we may need to prepare a specific volume of solution containing a certain number of moles of solute. Or perhaps we need to calculate the change in concentration accompanying a change in the volume of a solution. The relationships necessary to solve problems of this sort are all related to **molarity (M)**, which is the number of moles of solute per liter of solution.

A general route for converting among the various units associated with solutions is shown below:

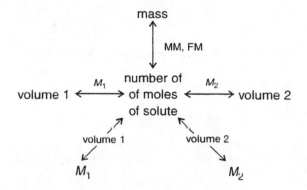

Example 1:   What volume of 0.050*M* NaCl solution contains 15 g of NaCl?

Answer: mass NaCl $\rightarrow$ number of moles of NaCl $\rightarrow$ volume NaCl

$$\text{volume NaCl, L} = 15\,\text{g NaCl} \left(\frac{1\,\text{mol NaCl}}{58.4\,\text{g NaCl}}\right)\left(\frac{1\,\text{L}}{0.050\,\text{mol NaCl}}\right) = 5.1\,\text{L}$$

Example 2:   How much HCl is required to prepare exactly 250 mL of a 0.150*M* solution?

Answer: *M* of HCl $\rightarrow$ number of moles of HCl $\rightarrow$ mass HCl

$$\text{mass HCl, g} = 250\,\text{mL solution} \left(\frac{0.150\,\text{mol HCl}}{1\,\text{L solution}}\right)\left(\frac{1\,\text{L}}{1000\,\text{mL}}\right)\left(\frac{36.5\,\text{g HCl}}{1\,\text{mol HCl}}\right) = 1.37\,\text{g HCl}$$

Note that the use of dimensional analysis in the preceding answer prevented an error of a factor of 10^3, by reminding us to change mL to L so that the units cancel properly.

Example 3:   If 100.0 mL of a 0.100*M* solution of KCl is diluted to 250.0 mL, what is the new concentration of the solution?

169

Answer: The route shows that the common link between M_1 and M_2 is the number of moles of solute. Set up your calculation this way: $M_1 \rightarrow$ number of moles $\rightarrow M_2$. Note that to get from M_1 to number of moles, we must *multiply* by volume, but to get from number of moles to M_2, we must *divide* by volume.

$$\text{new concentration of KCl} = \left(\frac{0.100 \text{ mol KCl}}{1 \text{ L solution}_1}\right)(100.0 \text{ mL solution}_1)\left(\frac{1}{250.0 \text{ mL solution}_2}\right) = 0.0400 M$$

Because the mL cancel, it is not necessary to convert mL to L in this case.

For chemical reactions in solution, the general route for calculations is:

volume of solution containing A $\xleftrightarrow{M_A}$ number of moles of A $\xleftrightarrow{\text{coefficients in equation}}$ number of moles of B $\xleftrightarrow{M_B}$ volume of solution containing B

↑ volume of solution containing A ↓ M_A

↑ volume of solution containing B ↓ M_B

Example 4: For the reaction,

$$\text{KOH(aq)} + \text{HCl(aq)} \rightarrow \text{KCl(aq)} + H_2O(l)$$

what volume of 0.150M KOH is required to react completely with 50.00 mL of 0.300M HCl?

Answer: The route to follow is:

volume of HCl solution $\rightarrow$ number of moles of HCl $\rightarrow$ number of moles of KOH $\rightarrow$ volume of KOH solution

$$\text{volume of KOH solution, mL} = 50.00 \text{ mL HCl} \left(\frac{1 \text{ L}}{1000 \text{ mL}}\right)\left(\frac{0.300 \text{ mol HCl}}{1 \text{ L solution}}\right)\left(\frac{1 \text{ mol KOH}}{1 \text{ mol HCl}}\right)\left(\frac{1 \text{ L solution}}{0.150 \text{ mol KOH}}\right)\left(\frac{1000 \text{ mL}}{1 \text{ L}}\right) = 100.0 \text{ mL}$$

Example 5: For the reaction

$$2\text{ NaOH(aq)} + H_2SO_4\text{(aq)} \rightarrow Na_2SO_4\text{(aq)} + 2\text{ }H_2O(l)$$

4.5 mL of 0.100M H_2SO_4 is required to completely react with 10.0 mL of a NaOH solution. What is the concentration of the NaOH solution?

Answer: The route to follow is:

volume of H_2SO_4 solution $\rightarrow$ number of moles of H_2SO_4 $\rightarrow$ number of moles of NaOH $\rightarrow$ M of NaOH solution

$$M \text{ of NaOH solution, } M = \frac{\text{number of moles of NaOH}}{1 \text{ L NaOH solution}} = \frac{0.0045 \text{ L } H_2SO_4 \text{ solution}}{} \left(\frac{0.100 \text{ mol } H_2SO_4}{1 \text{ L } H_2SO_4 \text{ solution}}\right)\left(\frac{2 \text{ mol NaOH}}{1 \text{ mol } H_2SO_4}\right)\left(\frac{1}{0.0100 \text{ L NaOH solution}}\right) = 0.090 M$$

Note that dimensional analysis reminded us that 2 mol of NaOH react with 1 mol of H_2SO_4.

Problem Set 5

5.1 Calculate the new concentration of the solution when:

(a) 25.0 mL of 1.43M HCl is diluted to 500.0 mL.

(b) 10.0 mL of 3.42M NaOH is diluted to 10.0 L.

(c) 450.0 mL of 0.20M H_2SO_4 is evaporated to a volume of 90.0 mL.

(d) 60.0 mL of 0.450M NaCl is diluted to 90.0 mL.

5.2 What volume of each of the following solutions contains 0.150 mol of the solute?

(a) 0.0025M HCl   (b) 1.25M $ZnSO_4$

(c) 17.5M NH_4OH (d) 0.100M $CuCl_2$

5.3 What volume of 0.250M $Ba(OH)_2$ is required to completely react 100.0 mL of a 0.500M solution of the acid in each of the following reactions?

(a) $Ba(OH)_2(aq)$ + 2 $HCl(aq)$ →
$$BaCl_2(aq) + 2 H_2O(l)$$

(b) $Ba(OH)_2(aq)$ + $H_2SO_4(aq)$ →
$$BaSO_4(aq) + 2 H_2O(l)$$

(c) $Ba(OH)_2(aq)$ + $H_3PO_4(aq)$ →
$$BaHPO_4(aq) + 2 H_2O(l)$$

(d) 3 $Ba(OH)_2(aq)$ + 2 $H_3PO_4(aq)$ →
$$Ba_3(PO_4)_2(s) + 6 H_2O(l)$$

5.4 In each of the following acid–base reactions, 25.0 mL of an HCl solution (the acid) completely reacts 10.0 mL of a 0.100M solution of the second reactant (the base). Calculate the concentration of the HCl solution in each case.

(a) $HCl(aq)$ + $NH_4OH(aq)$ →
$$NH_4Cl(aq) + H_2O(l)$$

(b) 2 $HCl(aq)$ + $Ca(OH)_2(aq)$ →
$$CaCl_2(aq) + 2 H_2O(l)$$

(c) 4 $HCl(aq)$ + $NaAl(OH)_4(aq)$ →
$$AlCl_3(aq) + 4 H_2O(l) + NaCl(aq)$$

(d) 2 $HCl(aq)$ + $Na_2C_2O_4(aq)$ →
$$2 NaCl(aq) + H_2C_2O_4(aq)$$

Answers to Problem Sets

Problem Set 1

1.1 655.72 hr

1.2 215.9 cm

1.3 603 cm^2

1.4 6.8×10^7 min

1.5 0.53 gal

1.6 1.13 kg

1.7 6.06×10^{-9} in.

1.8 422 ft, 129 m

1.9 62 mi hr^{-1}

1.10 472 mL

1.11 8.604 lb gal^{-1}

1.12 3820. km

1.13 37.7 mi hr^{-1}

1.14 41.5 lb

1.15 20.5 in. Hg, 0.686 atm, 6.95×10^4 Pa

1.16 1.07×10^3 mi hr^{-1}

1.17 1.89 mg F$^-$

1.18 322 min

1.19 5679 °F

1.20 0.697 g mL^{-1}

1.21 425 kg, 937 lb

1.22 50 °C, 323 K

Problem Set 2

2.1 (a) 2.083 mol   (b) 1.020 mol   (c) 0.3224 mol
(d) 0.2921 mol   (e) 0.5076 mol

2.2 (a) 72 g   (b) 39 g   (c) 40 g   (d) 29 g
(e) 39 g

2.3 (a) 3.764×10^{24} ions
(b) 1.882×10^{24} molecules
(c) 1.494×10^{24} molecules
(d) 3.101×10^{23} molecules
(e) 1.210×10^{23} molecules

2.4 (a) 5.66 g   (b) 53.8 g   (c) 59.5 g   (d) 96.7 g
(e) 45.5 g

Problem Set 3

3.1 (a) HO, H_2O_2 (b) SiH_3, Si_2H_6
(c) $C_7H_5O_2$, $C_{14}H_{10}O_4$ (d) P_2S_5, P_4S_{10}
(e) $C_5H_{10}NS_2$, $C_{10}H_{20}N_2S_4$
(f) Al_2O_3, Al_2O_3

3.2 (a) 15.95% B, 84.05% F
(b) 60.04% K, 18.45% C, 21.51% N
(c) 58.84% Ba, 13.74% S, 27.42% O
(d) 34.38% Ni, 28.14% C, 37.48% O
(e) 11.11% N, 3.20% H, 41.26% Cr, 44.43% O

Problem Set 4

4.1 (a) 46.08 g   (b) 211.2 g   (c) 234.9 g
(d) 22.56 g   (e) 56.21 g   (f) 133.2 g
(g) 357.9 g   (h) 68.20 g

4.2 (a) K, 143.5   (b) F_2, 147.3 g
(c) O_2, 75.02 g   (d) Fe_2O_3, 69.94 g
(e) CaC_2, 115.6 g   (f) HF, 130.1 g
(g) O_2, 84.64 g   (h) $BaCl_2$, 56.13 g

Problem Set 5

5.1 (a) 0.0715M (b) 0.00342M (c) 1.00M
(d) 0.300M

5.2 (a) 60.0 L   (b) 0.120 L or 120 mL
(c) 0.00857 L or 8.57 mL   (d) 1.50 L

5.3 (a) 100.0 mL   (b) 200.0 mL   (c) 200.0 mL
(d) 300.0 mL

5.4 (a) 0.0400M (b) 0.0800M (c) 0.160M
(d) 0.0800M

WORKSHEET 3

Formula Writing

This worksheet will introduce you to formula writing. Your work here will be confined to writing formulas of compounds when given the names of the compounds. Although it is a related skill, we will not attempt to name compounds from their formulas in this worksheet.

IONIC COMPOUNDS

Many of the substances you will study in the laboratory are composed of ions. An *ion* is an atom or group of atoms bearing a net charge other than zero. The charge on an ion is the result of an unequal number of smaller charged particles known as protons and electrons. Protons have an electrical charge of +1, while electrons have a −1 charge. Depending upon the number of each, an ion may have either a positive or negative charge, and the magnitude of each depends upon the difference between them. For example, an ion that contains 12 protons and 10 electrons would have a charge of +2: $12(+1) + 10(-1) = +2$. On the other hand, an ion that contains 17 protons and 18 electrons has a charge of −1: $17(+1) + 18(-1) = -1$. Those ions whose net charge is positive are known as *cations*. Negatively charged ions are called *anions*.

The table on the inside cover at the back of this manual includes the names and formulas of all the important ions you will need for this course. Examination of the ions in the table will reveal several items of importance. First, the charge on each ion is written in the upper right-hand corner. In addition, some of the ions are composed of just one atom; others contain several atoms. Those ions with one atom are *monatomic* ions, and those with two or more atoms are known as *polyatomic* ions.

Further examination of the polyatomic anions will reveal that many of them are composed of two elements, one of which is oxygen and the other is some other element. These ions are known as *oxyanions*. The nitrate, NO_3^-, sulfate, SO_4^{2-}, and phosphate, PO_4^{3-}, ions are examples of oxyanions.

You may also notice that some of the elements that form monatomic cations are found with more than one possible charge. For example, iron is found as either iron(II), Fe^{2+}, or iron(III), Fe^{3+}. The Roman numeral matches the charge on the ion, and it is included in the name of the ion to distinguish these two types of iron ion. Copper, cobalt, and lead are other examples of metal cations that exist in more than one form. On the other hand, those metals that form only one type of ion do not have any Roman numeral included in their names, because there is no need to distinguish between various types.

We refer to compounds that are made up of ions as *ionic compounds*. *The formula of an ionic compound consists of the simplest whole number ratio of ions that results in an uncharged formula.* For example, sodium chloride is made up of sodium ion, Na^+, and chloride ion, Cl^-. A 1:1 ratio of these ions results in a neutral charge. The formula of sodium chloride is NaCl:

$$Na^+ + Cl^- \quad \text{form} \quad NaCl$$

On the other hand, magnesium bromide is composed of magnesium ion, Mg^{2+}, and bromide ion, Br^-. These ions combine in a 2:1 ratio:

$$Mg^{2+} + 2\,Br^- \quad \text{form} \quad MgBr_2$$

Aluminum oxide must be composed of aluminum ion, Al^{3+}, and oxide ion, O^{2-}, in a 2:3 ratio:

$$2\,Al^{3+} + 3\,O^{2-} \quad \text{form} \quad Al_2O_3$$

Notice that the charges of the ions are not included in the formula of the compound. However, the number of ions of each type is written as a subscript to the right of each element. Finally, *the cation always appears first, both in the name of the compound and in its formula.*

The formulas for compounds composed from metals with a variable charge are written in exactly the same way. For example, copper(I) sulfide is composed of a 1:2 ratio of copper(I) and sulfide ions:

$$2\,Cu^+ + S^{2-} \quad \text{form} \quad Cu_2S$$

When polyatomic ions are present in a compound, formula writing may be slightly more complex. If the simplest whole number ratio includes only one polyatomic ion, the formula is obtained as previously explained. For example, potassium phosphate is composed of a 3:1 ratio of potassium ion and phosphate ion:

$$3\,K^+ + PO_4{}^{3-} \quad \text{form} \quad K_3PO_4$$

When more than one multiple of the polyatomic ion must be included in the formula, however, parentheses are used to maintain the identity of the polyatomic ion. Thus, the formula of calcium hydroxide is written with parentheses around the hydroxide ion. The subscript outside the parentheses indicates the presence of two hydroxides in the formula:

$$Ca^{2+} + 2\,OH^- \quad \text{form} \quad Ca(OH)_2$$

Similarly, the formula of iron(III) nitrate is:

$$Fe^{3+} + 3\,NO_3^- \quad \text{form} \quad Fe(NO_3)_3$$

NONIONIC COMPOUNDS
(NONMETALS ONLY)

Many nonionic compounds are named using a prefix system. The following prefixes have the numerical meanings indicated:

mono = 1		hexa = 6	
di = 2		hepta = 7	
tri = 3		octa = 8	
tetra = 4		nona = 9	
penta = 5		deca = 10	

The names of compounds using this system are easily interpreted. For example, the following names and formulas correspond to one another:

carbon monoxide	CO
carbon dioxide	CO_2
sulfur trioxide	SO_3
diphosphorus pentoxide	P_2O_5
carbon tetrachloride	CCl_4
nitrogen triiodide	NI_3

Notice that all of these compounds end in -*ide*. Also notice that prefixes were not used *at all* for the ionic compounds named earlier.

ACIDS AND BASES

The common laboratory acids are derived from the simplest whole number ratio of hydrogen ion, H^+, and one of the anions discussed earlier. The names and formulas of acids are sufficiently detailed that we will not give a comprehensive treatment here. However, the most common acids and their formulas are the following:

hydrochloric acid:	$H^+ + Cl^- = HCl$
nitric acid:	$H^+ + NO_3^- = HNO_3$
sulfuric acid:	$2\,H^+ + SO_4^{2-} = H_2SO_4$
phosphoric acid:	$3\,H^+ + PO_3^{3-} = H_3PO_4$
acetic acid:	$H^+ + C_2H_3O_2^- = HC_2H_3O_2$

The most common laboratory bases are derived from a metal ion and hydroxide. Two commonly used bases are sodium hydroxide, NaOH, and potassium hydroxide, KOH.

ELEMENTS

The formulas of most elements are simply the symbols of their atoms. For example, all of the metals and noble gases are written as monatomic substances:

helium	He	potassium	K
neon	Ne	calcium	Ca
argon	Ar	iron	Fe

However, there are seven elements that occur as diatomic molecules:

hydrogen	H_2	chlorine	Cl_2
nitrogen	N_2	bromine	Br_2
oxygen	O_2	iodine	I_2
fluorine	F_2		

In addition, elemental phosphorus is tetratomic, P_4, and sulfur forms octatomic molecules, S_8. For simplicity, however, elemental sulfur is generally written in monatomic form, S.

COMMON NAMES

Many substances are known by names that have no simple system of nomenclature. You will find it essential to know the formulas of two such substances: water, H_2O, and ammonia, NH_3.

WORKSHEET 3

Formula Writing

1. Write formulas for the following compounds:

   (a) potassium bromide _____

   (b) lithium sulfide _____

   (c) calcium fluoride _____

   (d) barium oxide _____

   (e) magnesium nitride _____

   (f) aluminum sulfide _____

2. Write formulas for the following compounds:

   (a) copper(I) iodide _____

   (b) copper(II) iodide _____

   (c) iron(II) sulfide _____

   (d) iron(III) sulfide _____

   (e) cobalt(III) chloride _____

   (f) lead(IV) oxide _____

3. Write formulas for the following compounds:

   (a) sodium nitrate _____

   (b) sodium sulfate _____

   (c) calcium nitrate _____

   (d) potassium phosphate _____

   (e) ammonium nitrate _____

   (f) ammonium sulfate _____

   (g) potassium chromate _____

   (h) ammonium chromate _____

Vorksheet 3 (continued)

1. Write formulas for the following compounds:

(a) iron(III) hydroxide _____

(b) copper(I) sulfate _____

(c) zinc carbonate _____

(d) sodium hydrogen carbonate _____

(e) magnesium cyanide _____

(f) lead(IV) sulfate _____

5. Write formulas for the following compounds:

(a) nitrogen monoxide _____

(b) carbon disulfide _____

(c) boron trifluoride _____

(d) dinitrogen tetroxide _____

(e) sulfur dioxide _____

(f) phosphorus trichloride _____

(g) diphosphorus pentasulfide _____

5. Write formulas for the following compounds:

(a) hydrochloric acid _____

(b) nitric acid _____

(c) sulfuric acid _____

(d) phosphoric acid _____

(e) acetic acid _____

7. Write the formulas of the following elements:

(a) hydrogen _____

(b) magnesium _____

(c) chlorine _____

NAME: ______________________________ DATE: __________

Worksheet 3 (continued)

(d) phosphorus ____________

(e) oxygen ____________

(f) sodium ____________

(g) bromine ____________

(h) nitrogen ____________

(i) neon ____________

(j) helium ____________

(k) iodine ____________

(l) lead ____________

8. Write formulas of the following well-known substances:

(a) water ____________

(b) ammonia ____________

WORKSHEET
4

Chemical Equations

Most of the work you carry out in the laboratory involves chemical chan When a chemical change takes place, substances known as *reactants* underg change to form new substances known as *products*. The chemical equation symbolic device used to represent such changes. For example, the follow chemical equation represents the reaction of hydrogen and oxygen to fe water:

$$2 H_2 + O_2 \rightarrow 2 H_2O$$

Examination of this chemical equation reveals a number of featu common to all chemical equations. First, each substance is represented by chemical formula. In the cases of hydrogen and oxygen, these elements diatomic. Notice that the reactants (hydrogen and oxygen) are on the left of the equation, and the products (water) appear on the right. The reacta and products are separated from one another by an arrow that may interpreted as "form" or "react to form." In addition, substances appearing the same side of the arrow are further separated from one another by a plus sign.

Continuing our examination, notice the presence of coefficients (number 2) in front of hydrogen and water. Although no coefficient is writter front of oxygen, the coefficient 1 is understood when nothing has been writt This chemical equation says that "two molecules of hydrogen plus one molec of oxygen react to form two molecules of water." A careful examination of equation reveals that the number of hydrogen atoms (four) and oxygen atc (two) are the same on both sides of the arrow. Because the number of atom: each element are the same on both sides of the equation, we call this a *balan equation.*

This worksheet will introduce you to the process of interpreting description of a reaction, writing a chemical equation for the reaction, a balancing the equation by adjusting the coefficients. You will also be introdu to some additional symbolism that may be included in chemical equations.

BALANCING CHEMICAL EQUATIONS

Let us consider the following statement, which describes a process that occurs when natural gas burns:

> Methane (CH_4) burns in the presence of oxygen to form carbon dioxide and water.

We may represent this statement with the following word equation:

> methane + oxygen → carbon dioxide + water

Next, we will substitute the correct chemical formula for each substance:

$$CH_4 + O_2 \rightarrow CO_2 + H_2O \quad \text{(unbalanced equation)}$$

Although we have written the correct formulas for each reactant and product, notice that the number of hydrogen atoms and oxygen atoms is not the same on both sides of the equation. The equation we have just written is an *unbalanced equation*. To balance the equation, we must adjust the coefficients. Adjusting the coefficients adjusts the ratios of reactants and products in the equation so that the number of atoms of each element is the same on both sides of the arrow.

To show how to balance an equation, we will put a blank space in front of each formula in the unbalanced equation, so that we can keep track of which coefficients we have already assigned and which have not yet been determined:

$$\underline{\quad} CH_4 + \underline{\quad} O_2 \rightarrow \underline{\quad} CO_2 + \underline{\quad} H_2O$$

In order to get started, let us assume that one molecule of CH_4 reacts:

$$\underline{1} CH_4 + \underline{\quad} O_2 \rightarrow \underline{\quad} CO_2 + \underline{\quad} H_2O$$

Since 1 CH_4 contains 1 atom of C, we will balance the carbon by placing a coefficient of 1 in front of CO_2 on the right. One molecule of CH_4 also contains 4 atoms of H. Since each H_2O on the right has two hydrogen atoms, a coefficient of 2 in front of H_2O will balance the hydrogens ($2 \times 2 = 4$):

$$\underline{1} CH_4 + \underline{\quad} O_2 \rightarrow \underline{1} CO_2 + \underline{2} H_2O$$

To complete the equation, we must balance the oxygen. Since we have assigned coefficients to all of the products, the number of oxygen atoms on the right may be determined: 1 CO_2 contains 2 oxygen atoms and 2 H_2O also contains 2 oxygen atoms. Thus, there is a total of 4 oxygen atoms on the right. On the left, oxygen atoms come in pairs, as O_2. To balance the oxygen, there must be 2 O_2 on the left:

$$\underline{1} CH_4 + \underline{2} O_2 \rightarrow \underline{1} CO_2 + \underline{2} H_2O \text{ (balanced equation)}$$

In practice, we would not write the coefficients of 1, but instead, the final form of the equation would be presented as:

$$CH_4 + 2 O_2 \rightarrow CO_2 + 2 H_2O \quad \text{(balanced equation)}$$

Let us balance a similar equation, the combustion of propane (C_3H_8) in oxygen to form carbon dioxide and water. The word *combustion* refers to a type of reaction that usually indicates that burning occurs:

propane + oxygen → carbon dioxide + water

_____ C_3H_8 + _____ O_2 → _____ CO_2 + _____ H_2O

As a general rule, it is often easiest to begin by assigning a coefficient of 1 to the most complicated substance in the unbalanced equation:

__1__ C_3H_8 + _____ O_2 → _____ CO_2 + _____ H_2O

Since 1 C_3H_8 contains 3 atoms of C and 8 atoms of H, we can balance these elements by assigning a coefficient of 3 to the CO_2 and 4 to the H_2O:

__1__ C_3H_8 + _____ O_2 → __3__ CO_2 + __4__ H_2O

These assignments result in: $(3 \times 2) + (4 \times 1) = 10$ atoms of oxygen on the right. To balance the oxygen, we must assign a coefficient of 5 in front of the O_2 on the left:

__1__ C_3H_8 + __5__ O_2 → __3__ CO_2 + __4__ H_2O

As a final example, consider the reaction of iron(III) sulfide with oxygen to form iron(III) oxide and sulfur dioxide:

_____ Fe_2S_3 + _____ O_2 → _____ Fe_2O_3 + _____ SO_2

If a coefficient of 1 is assigned to Fe_2S_3, there will be 2 atoms of Fe and 3 atoms of S on the left. These may be balanced by assigning a coefficient of 1 to Fe_2O_3 and 3 to SO_2:

__1__ Fe_2S_3 + _____ O_2 → __1__ Fe_2O_3 + __3__ SO_2

However, this results in 9 atoms of oxygen on the right. Since the oxygen molecules on the left are diatomic, we must take oxygen atoms in pairs. This would require a fractional coefficient of either 9/2 or 4.5. However, the use of fractional coefficients is considered incorrect form for most purposes. A *correctly balanced equation gives the simplest whole number ratio of coefficients that balances the equation.* To remove the fractional coefficients, we simply double all of the coefficients, leading to the following balanced equation:

__2__ Fe_2S_3 + __9__ O_2 → __2__ Fe_2O_3 + __6__ SO_2

There are several additional symbols that you are likely to encounter in chemical equations. These are known as *state symbols*, and they tell what physical state the substance is in. There are four such symbols: (s) = solid, (l) = liquid, (g) = gaseous, and (aq) = aqueous. The aqueous symbol is used to indicate when a substance is dissolved in water. The appropriate symbol is added to the formula of each reactant and product, following its final subscript. For example, aqueous potassium nitrate is written as $KNO_3(aq)$.

Using state symbols, we can write the following balanced equation describing the reaction of solid magnesium carbonate with aqueous hydrochloric acid to form aqueous magnesium chloride, liquid water, and carbon dioxide gas:

$$MgCO_3(s) + 2\ HCl(aq) \rightarrow MgCl_2(aq) + H_2O(l) + CO_2(g)$$

State symbols can also be used to describe a phase change, such as the melting of ice:

$$H_2O(s) \rightarrow H_2O(l)$$

or the process of dissolving a substance in water:

$$HCl(g) \rightarrow HCl(aq)$$

Much of your laboratory work will involve the formation of insoluble solid products known as precipitates. For example, when an aqueous solution of sodium chloride is mixed with an aqueous silver nitrate solution, a precipitate of silver chloride forms, leaving sodium nitrate in aqueous solution:

$$NaCl(aq) + AgNO_3(aq) \rightarrow AgCl(s) + NaNO_3(aq)$$

The use of state symbols in this manual is reserved for those situations where they are needed for clarity.

WORKSHEET 4

Chemical Equations

1. Balance the following equations:

   (a) ___ $Ba(OH)_2$ + ___ H_2SO_4 → ___ $BaSO_4$ + ___ H_2O

   (b) ___ N_2H_4 + ___ O_2 → ___ NO_2 + ___ H_2O

   (c) ___ Zn + ___ $AgNO_3$ → ___ $Zn(NO_3)_2$ + ___ Ag

   (d) ___ H_3PO_4 + ___ KOH → ___ K_3PO_4 + ___ H_2O

   (e) ___ Al + ___ HBr → ___ $AlBr_3$ + ___ H_2

   (f) ___ $CaCO_3$ + ___ HNO_3 → ___ $Ca(NO_3)_2$ + ___ H_2O + ___ CO_2

   (g) ___ C_4H_{10} + ___ O_2 → ___ CO_2 + ___ H_2O

   (h) ___ Mg_3N_2 + ___ H_2O → ___ NH_3 + ___ MgO

2. Convert the following word equations into balanced chemical equations. (If you need to review formula writing, refer to the discussion for Worksheet 2.)

   (a) zinc + hydrochloric acid → zinc chloride + hydrogen

   (b) barium hydroxide + carbon dioxide → barium carbonate + water

   (c) magnesium oxide + nitric acid → magnesium nitrate + water

   (d) sodium + water → sodium hydroxide + hydrogen

   (e) magnesium carbonate + sulfuric acid → magnesium sulfate + carbon dioxide + water

   (f) nitrogen + hydrogen → ammonia

orksheet 4 (continued)

(g) phosphoric acid + calcium hydroxide → calcium phosphate + water

(h) magnesium + nitrogen → magnesium nitride

Use state symbols to write balanced equations describing the following changes:

(a) Solid potassium metal reacts with liquid water to form aqueous potassium hydroxide and hydrogen gas.

(b) Aqueous potassium chromate reacts with aqueous lead(II) nitrate to form a solid precipitate of lead(II) chromate and an aqueous solution of potassium nitrate.

(c) Solid sodium metal melts.

(d) When gaseous carbon dioxide is bubbled through aqueous calcium hydroxide, both liquid water and a solid precipitate of calcium carbonate form.

(e) Solid sodium hydroxide dissolves in water.

(f) Aqueous sulfuric acid reacts with aqueous barium hydroxide to form a precipitate of solid barium sulfate and liquid water.

(g) Dry ice sublimes. (Remember, dry ice is solid carbon dioxide. Sublimation is the process of passing from the solid state directly to the gaseous state.)

WORKSHEET
5

Chemical
Calculations

This worksheet will provide practice in several important calculations you will use in your laboratory work: calculating molecular masses, calculating moles, and calculating the molarities of solutions.

MOLECULAR MASSES

Every element has an atomic mass, which represents the average mass of an atom of the element compared to a standard known as carbon-12. For the purpose of this discussion, you will need to be able to look up the atomic mass of each element on the periodic table (see inside front cover). If you examine the periodic table, you will find that the symbol for each element is in a box that also contains an integer (the atomic number) and a decimal number. The decimal number is the atomic mass. Check the periodic table and be sure that you can find the following atomic masses:

$$H = 1.008 \qquad O = 15.999$$

$$C = 12.011 \qquad F = 18.998$$

$$N = 14.007 \qquad Cl = 35.453$$

As a convention for this laboratory manual and the accompanying text, we will round off atomic masses to the nearest 0.1. Rounding off the atomic masses for these elements gives the following values:

$$H = 1.0 \qquad O = 16.0$$

$$C = 12.0 \qquad F = 19.0$$

$$N = 14.0 \qquad Cl = 35.5$$

The molecular mass of a substance is simply the sum of the atomic masses of the atoms present in its chemical formula. For example, the molecular mass of water, H_2O, would be calculated as follows:

$$2 \times H = 2 \times 1.0 = 2.0$$
$$\underline{1 \times O = 1 \times 16.0 = 16.0}$$
$$H_2O \qquad\qquad = 18.0$$

Similarly, the molecular mass of $C_3H_6F_2$ is:

$$3 \times C = 3 \times 12.0 = 36.0$$
$$6 \times H = 6 \times 1.0 = 6.0$$
$$\underline{2 \times F = 2 \times 19.0 = 38.0}$$
$$C_3H_6F_2 \qquad\qquad = 80.0$$

Although ionic substances such as sodium sulfate, Na_2SO_4, do not form distinct molecules, we occasionally refer to the sum of the atomic masses in their formulas as molecular masses in this manual. The term *formula mass* is often used instead of molecular mass for such compounds.

MOLES

The sizes and masses of atoms and molecules are so small that most of our laboratory work requires us to work with samples that contain rather large numbers of molecules. The basic unit we work with is known as the mole (mol). Like a dozen (which means 12) or a gross (which means 144), the mole represents a number. One mole is equal to 6.02×10^{23}. This number is also known as Avogadro's number. One mole of a molecular substance contains Avogadro's number of molecules. (One mole of atoms contains Avogadro's number of atoms.) When we carry out laboratory work, we will be working with quantities that can be measured in terms of moles.

For the purposes of our calculations, there is an operational definition that will be helpful for you to learn: *One mole of a molecular substance is equal to its molecular mass, taken in grams.* By this definition, 1 mole of water has a mass of 18.0 grams. Similarly, 1 mole of $C_3H_6F_2$ has a mass of 80.0 grams:

$$1 \text{ mol } H_2O = 18.0 \text{ g } H_2O$$

$$1 \text{ mol } C_3H_6F_2 = 80.0 \text{ g } C_3H_6F_2$$

Since these quantities represent the mass of 1 mole, each is referred to as the *molar mass:* the mass per mole. Numerically, the molar mass is equal to the molecular mass in units of grams per mole.

To calculate the number of moles in a sample, we may use the molar mass as a conversion factor between grams and moles. For example, if 18.0 g H_2O equals 1 mole, it follows that 36.0 H_2O equal 2 moles. We can use dimensional analysis to carry out this calculation in a systematic fashion:

$$1 \text{ mol } H_2O = 18.0 \text{ g } H_2O$$

$$? \text{ mol } H_2O = 36.0 \text{ g } H_2O \left(\frac{1 \text{ mol } H_2O}{18.0 \text{ g } H_2O} \right) = 2.00 \text{ mol } H_2O$$

The number of moles in 12.0 g $C_3H_6F_2$ may be calculated in a similar fashion, using the molar mass calculated earlier:

$$1 \text{ mol } C_3H_6F_2 = 80.0 \text{ g } C_3H_6F_2$$

$$? \text{ mol } C_3H_6F_2 = 12.0 \text{ g } C_3H_6F_2 \left(\frac{1 \text{ mol } C_3H_6F_2}{80.0 \text{ g } C_3H_6F_2} \right) = 0.150 \text{ mol } C_3H_6F_2$$

MOLARITY

Much of the work you will carry out in the laboratory involves the use of solutions. A *solution* is a homogeneous mixture. As a general rule, the solutions you will work with have a substance, known as a *solute*, dissolved in a liquid, known as the *solvent*. Furthermore, most of the solutions you will use are aqueous solutions: those for which the solvent is water. For example, salt water is an aqueous solution of sodium chloride.

In the laboratory, it is helpful to know the concentrations of the solutions with which we work. The concentration tells the amount of solute dissolved in a given amount of the solution. The most informative unit of concentration is molarity, the number of moles per liter:

$$\text{molarity} = \frac{\text{moles of solute}}{\text{liters of solution}}$$

The symbol M is used to designate molarity.

To prepare 1 liter of a 1 molar (1 M) solution, we would measure out 1 mole of the desired solute and add enough water to make a total volume of 1 liter. Notice that we do not mix 1 mole of solute and 1 liter of solvent (in this case, water). That would probably result in a total volume greater than 1 liter, giving a concentration less than 1 M. Instead, we add *enough* water to achieve the desired volume.

To calculate the molarity of a solution, we need to known the number of moles of solute and the total volume of solution in which it is dissolved. For example, suppose 33.2 g of KI is dissolved in enough water to prepare 0.250 L of solution. To calculate the molarity, we will first calculate the number of moles of KI:

$$? \text{ mol KI} = 33.2 \text{ g KI} \left(\frac{1 \text{ mol KI}}{166.0 \text{ g KI}} \right) = 0.200 \text{ mol KI}$$

Then, we will divide the number of moles by the number of liters of solution:

$$\text{molarity} = \frac{0.200 \text{ mol KI}}{0.250 \text{ L soln}} = 0.800 \ M \text{ KI}$$

The molarity of a glucose solution prepared by dissolving 9.00 g $C_6H_{12}O_6$ in enough water to make 125 mL would be calculated similarly. First, we will calculate the number of moles of glucose:

$$? \text{ mol } C_6H_{12}O_6 = 9.00 \text{ g } C_6H_{12}O_6 \left(\frac{1 \text{ mol } C_6H_{12}O_6}{180.0 \text{ g } C_6H_{12}O_6} \right)$$

$$= 0.0500 \text{ mol } C_6H_{12}O_6$$

Before calculating the molarity, however, we must convert 125 mL to 0.125 L:

$$\text{molarity} = \frac{0.0500 \text{ mol } C_6H_{12}O_6}{0.125 \text{ L soln}} = 0.400 \ M \ C_6H_{12}O_6$$

The concentrations of most of the solutions you work with in the laboratory will be expressed in terms of their molarities.

NAME: ______________________________ DATE: __________

Worksheet 5 (continued)

(b) 23.4 g NaCl

(c) 15.0 g K_2CO_3

(d) 9.63 g H_3PO_4

(e) 7.10 g $Mg(OH)_2$

3. Calculate the molarities of the following solutions:

(a) 34.0 g NH_3 in a total volume of 1.25 L soln

(b) 11.0 g HBr in a total volume of 675 mL

(c) 7.50 g NaCl in a total volume of 325 mL

NAME: ______________________________ DATE: __________

WORKSHEET 5

Chemical Calculations

1. Calculate the molecular or formula masses of the following substances:

   (a) C_3H_8

   (b) NaCl

   (c) K_2CO_3

   (d) H_3PO_4

   (e) $Mg(OH)_2$

2. Use your answers from question 1 to help you calculate the number of moles in each of the following:

   (a) 176 g C_3H_8

APPENDIX
A

Conversions and Prefixes

MASS SI unit is the kilogram (kg)	LENGTH SI unit is the meter (m)	VOLUME SI unit is the cubic meter (m³)
1 kg = 1000 g	1 m = 100 cm	1 liter (L) = 1000 mL
1 kg = 2.2046 lb	1 m = 1000 mm	1 L = 0.001 m³
1 lb = 453.6 g	1 m = 39.37 in	1 L = 1.057 qt
1 lb = 16 oz	1 km = 1000 m	1 mL = 1 cm³
1 ton = 2000 lb	1 mi = 5280 ft	1 qt = 32 oz
	1 mi = 1.609 km	1 gal = 4 qt
	1 in = 2.54 cm	

PRESSURE SI unit is the Pascal (Pa)	TEMPERATURE SI unit is the kelvin (K)	METRIC PREFIXES	
		pico (p)	= 10^{-12}
		nano (n)	= 10^{-9}
1 atm = 101.3 kPa	0 K = - 273.15 °C	micro (μ)	= 10^{-6}
1 atm = 760 torr	K = °C + 273.15	milli (m)	= 10^{-3}
1 atm = 14.70 lb/in²	°C = 5/9 (°F - 32)	centi (c)	= 10^{-2}
1 torr = 1 mm Hg		deci (d)	= 10^{-1}
		kilo (k)	= 10^{3}
		mega (M)	= 10^{6}

APPENDIX
B

Vapor Pressure of Water

TEMPERATURE (° C)	VAPOR PRESSURE (TORR)	
10	9.2	
15	12.8	
16	13.6	
17	14.5	
18	15.5	
19	16.5	
20	17.5	
21	18.7	
22	19.8	
23	21.1	
24	22.4	
25	23.8	1 atmosphere = 760 torr
26	25.2	= 760 mm Hg
27	26.7	= 76 cm Hg
28	28.3	= 101.3 kPa
29	30.0	
30	31.8	
31	33.7	1 mm Hg = 13.59 mm H$_2$O
32	35.7	
33	37.7	
34	39.9	
35	42.2	
40	55.3	
45	71.9	
50	92.5	
60	149.4	
70	233.7	
80	355.1	
90	525.8	
95	633.9	
100	760.0	
105	906.1	

Solubility Rules

Nitrates
All nitrate salts are soluble.

Alkali metals
The salts of lithium, sodium, potassium, rubidium, and cesium are generally very soluble.

Ammonium salts
Almost all ammonium salts are soluble.

Sulfates
The sulfates of most common elements are soluble, with the exception of calcium, strontium, barium, and lead (II) ions. Silver sulfate is slightly soluble.

Hydroxides
Most hydroxides are insoluble except those of the alkali metals and barium. Calcium hydroxide is slightly soluble.

Halides
Chloride, bromide, and iodide salts are generally soluble except those of silver, lead (II), and mercury (I) ions.

Sulfides
Most sulfides are insoluble except those of the alkali metals and ammonium ion.

Acetates
All acetates are soluble except silver acetate, which is slightly soluble.

Silver salts
All silver salts are insoluble except silver nitrate, $AgNO_3$; silver nitrite, $AgNO_2$; and silver perchlorate, $AgClO_4$. Silver acetate, $AgC_2H_3O_2$, and silver sulfate, Ag_2SO_4, are slightly soluble.

Carbonates
All carbonates are insoluble except those of ammonium, sodium, potassium, and the other alkali metals.

Phosphates
Phosphates are insoluble except those of ammonium, sodium, potassium and other alkali metals.

Periodic Table of the Elements

Legend:
- atomic name
- atomic number
- element symbol
- atomic mass

Example:
boron
5
B
10.811

= metals
= nonmetals
= metaloids

1A (1)	2A (2)	3B (3)	4B (4)	5B (5)	6B (6)	7B (7)	8B (8)	8B (9)	8B (10)	1B (11)	2B (12)	3A (13)	4A (14)	5A (15)	6A (16)	7A (17)	8A (18)
hydrogen 1 H 1.0079																	helium 2 He 4.0026
lithium 3 Li 6.941	beryllium 4 Be 9.0122											boron 5 B 10.811	carbon 6 C 12.011	nitrogen 7 N 14.0067	oxygen 8 O 15.9994	fluorine 9 F 18.9984	neon 10 Ne 20.1797
sodium 11 Na 22.9898	magnesium 12 Mg 24.3050											aluminum 13 Al 26.9815	silicon 14 Si 28.0855	phosphorous 15 P 30.9738	sulfur 16 S 32.066	chlorine 17 Cl 35.4527	argon 18 Ar 39.948
potassium 19 K 39.0983	calcium 20 Ca 40.078	scandium 21 Sc 44.9559	titanium 22 Ti 47.88	vanadium 23 V 50.9415	chromium 24 Cr 51.9961	manganese 25 Mn 54.9380	iron 26 Fe 55.847	cobalt 27 Co 58.9332	nickel 28 Ni 58.693	copper 29 Cu 63.546	zinc 30 Zn 65.39	gallium 31 Ga 69.723	germanium 32 Ge 72.61	arsenic 33 As 74.9216	selenium 34 Se 78.96	bromine 35 Br 79.904	krypton 36 Kr 83.80
rubidium 37 Rb 85.4678	strontium 38 Sr 87.62	yttrium 39 Y 88.9059	zirconium 40 Zr 91.224	niobium 41 Nb 92.9064	molybdenum 42 Mo 95.94	technetium 43 Tc (98)	ruthenium 44 Ru 101.07	rhodium 45 Rh 102.9055	palladium 46 Pd 106.42	silver 47 Ag 107.8682	cadmium 48 Cd 112.411	indium 49 In 114.82	tin 50 Sn 118.710	antimony 51 Sb 121.760	tellurium 52 Te 127.60	iodine 53 I 126.9045	xenon 54 Xe 131.29
cesium 55 Cs 132.9054	barium 56 Ba 137.327	lanthanum 57 La* 138.9055	hafnium 72 Hf 178.49	tantalum 73 Ta 180.9479	tungsten 74 W 183.85	rhenium 75 Re 186.207	osmium 76 Os 190.23	iridium 77 Ir 192.22	platinum 78 Pt 195.08	gold 79 Au 196.9665	mercury 80 Hg 200.59	thallium 81 Tl 204.3833	lead 82 Pb 207.2	bismuth 83 Bi 208.9804	polonium 84 Po (209)	astatine 85 At (210)	radon 86 Rn (222)
francium 87 Fr (223)	radium 88 Ra (226)	actinium 89 Ac† (227)	rutherfordium 104 Rf (261)	dubnium 105 Db (262)	seaborgium 106 Sg (263)	bohrium 107 Bh (262)	hassium 108 Hs (265)	meitnerium 109 Mt (266)	to be named 110 discovered Nov. 1994	to be named 111 discovered Dec. 1994	to be named 112 discovered Nov. 1995						

*Lanthanide series

cerium 58 Ce 140.115	praseodymium 59 Pr 140.9076	neodymium 60 Nd 144.24	promethium 61 Pm (145)	samarium 62 Sm 150.39	europium 63 Eu 151.965	gadolinium 64 Gd 157.25	terbium 65 Tb 158.9253	dysprosium 66 Dy 162.50	holmium 67 Ho 164.9303	erbium 68 Er 167.26	thulium 69 Tm 168.9342	ytterbium 70 Yb 173.04	lutetium 71 Lu 174.967

†Actinide series

thorium 90 Th 232.0381	protactinium 91 Pa 231.0359	uranium 92 U 238.0289	neptunium 93 Np (237)	plutonium 94 Pu (244)	americium 95 Am (243)	curium 96 Cm (247)	berkelium 97 Bk (247)	californium 98 Cf (251)	einsteinium 99 Es (252)	fermium 100 Fm (257)	mendelevium 101 Md (258)	nobelium 102 No (259)	lawrencium 103 Lr (262)

Atomic masses are 1993 IUPAC values. rounded to four decimal places. Those shown in parentheses are for the isotope with the longest half life.